Carpentry and joinery volume 1

C000280820

Carpentry and joinery volume 1

Brian Porter, L.C.G., A.I.O.C.
Department of Building Trades,
Leeds College of Building

Edward Arnold
A division of Hodder & Stoughton
LONDON NEW YORK MELBOURNE AUCKLAND

© 1982 Brian Porter

First published in Great Britain 1982
Reprinted 1984, 1987 (with amendments), 1988, 1989

British Library Cataloguing in Publication Data

Porter, Brian
  Carpentry and joinery.
  Vol. 1
  1. Carpentry 2. Joinery
  I. Title
  694   TH5606

ISBN 0-7131-3456-9

Typeset in 10/11pt English Times by Colset Private Ltd, Singapore.
Printed and bound in Great Britain for Edward Arnold, the
educational, academic and medical publishing division of Hodder
and Stoughton Limited, 41 Bedford Square, London WC1B 3DQ by
Richard Clay Ltd, Bungay, Suffolk.

Contents

Preface

This volume is the first of three designed to meet the needs of students engaged on a course of study in carpentry and joinery. Together, the three volumes cover the content of the City and Guilds of London Institute craft certificate course in carpentry and joinery (course number 585).

I have adopted a predominantly pictorial approach to the subject matter and have tried to integrate the discussion of craft theory and associated subjects such as geometry and mensuration so that their interdependence is apparent throughout. However, I have not attempted to offer instruction in sketching, drawing, and perspective techniques (BS 1192), which I think are best left to the individual student's school or college.

Procedures described in the practical sections of the text have been chosen because they follow safe working principles — this is not to say that there are no suitable alternatives, simply that I favour the ones chosen.

Finally, although the main aim of the book is to supplement school- or college-based work of a theoretical and practical nature, its presentation is such that it should also prove invaluable to students studying by correspondence course ('distance learning') and to mature students who in earlier years may perhaps have overlooked the all-important basic principles of our craft.

Brian Porter

Acknowledgements

I would like to thank my colleagues and friends at the Leeds College of Building for their help and guidance in compiling the text, and in particular Mr E. Judkins M.C.I.O.B., A.I.O.C., senior lecturer, for proof-reading this volume.

The photographs in figs 2.16 to 2.23, 2.41, 2.42, 2.44, 2.46 to 2.48, 2.52, 2.63 to 2.65, 2.76, 2.77, 2.79, 2.82, 2.83, and 2.94 were taken by J. H. Dwight and K. Proctor, and I am very grateful to them for their help.

I would also like to thank the following organisations for supplying technical information and, where noted, for their kind permission to reproduce photographs or illustrations:

G. Cartwright Ltd; CIBA-GEIGY (UK) Ltd; Crosby Windows Ltd (figs 11.2 and 11.5); Denford Machine Tools Ltd (fig. 4.23), Dominion Machinery Co. Ltd (figs 4.17 and 4.19); English Abrasives Ltd (Table 2.6); Fidor − Fibre Building Board − Development Organisation Ltd; Forestor − Forest and Sawmill − Equipment (Engineers) Ltd (fig. 1.5); Formica Ltd; GKN Screws and Fasteners Ltd; Rabone Chesterman Ltd; The Rawlplug Company Ltd (figs 14.9 to 14.13); Bahco Record Tools Ltd (figs 2.26 to 2.28, 2.30 to 2.35, 2.37, 2.53 to 2.61, 2.70 to 2.75, 2.93 to 2.96, 2.116, and 6.9); Thomas Robinson and Son Ltd (figs 4.1, 4.4, 4.5, 4.9, 4.12, 4.14); Spear and Jackson (Tools) Ltd; Stanley Tools Ltd (figs 2.29, 2.36, 2.38 to 2.40, 2.67, 2.80, 2.81, 2.86 to 2.89, and Table 2.5); Stenner of Tiverton Ltd (figs 1.9 and 1.11 to 1.13); The Swedish Finnish Timber Council (figs 1.6 and 1.7); The Timber Research and Development Association (TRADA); The Timber Trades Federation; W. Tyzack Sons and Turner Ltd; Wadkin Woodworking Machinery Ltd (figs 4.2, 4.7, 4.10, and 4.20), G. F. Wells Ltd (Timber Drying Engineers) (fig. 1.26); Wolf Electric Tools Ltd (figs 3.1, 3.3 to 3.8, 3.10 to 3.12, and 4.21).

Tables 1.2 and 1.4 are extracted from BS 4471:part 1:1978 and Table 1.3 is extracted from BS 5450:1977 by kind permission of the British Standards Institution, 2 Park St, London W1A 2BS, from whom copies of the complete standards may be obtained.

Finally, I must thank my wife − Hilary Yvonne − for her continual help, patience, and understanding during the writing of this book.

Brian Porter

1 Timber and associated materials

1.1 Growth and structure of a tree
The life of a tree begins very much like that of any other plant − the difference being that, if the seedling survives its early stage of growth to become a sapling (young tree), it may develop into one of the largest plants in the plant kingdom.

The hazards to young trees are many and varied. Animals are responsible for the destruction of many young saplings, but this is often regarded as a natural thinning-out of an otherwise overcrowded forest, thus allowing the sapling to mature and develop into a tree of natural size and shape. Where thinning has not taken place, trees grow thin and spindly − evidence of this can be seen in any overgrown woodland where trees have had to compete for the daylight necessary for their food production.

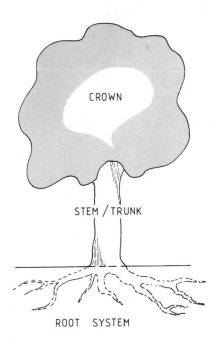

Fig. 1.1 Main parts of a tree

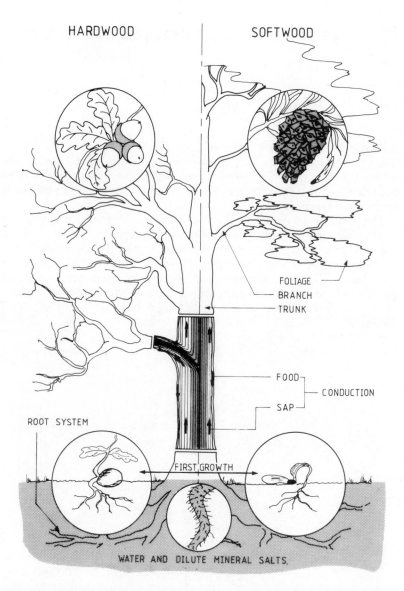

Fig. 1.2 Growth of a tree

With all natural resources which are in constant demand, there comes a time when demand outweighs supply. Fortunately, although trees require 30 to 100 years or more to mature, it is possible to ensure a continuing supply — provided that land is made available and felling (cutting down) is strictly controlled. This has meant that varying degrees of conservation have had to be enforced throughout some of the world's largest natural forests and has led to the development of massive man-made forests (forest farming).

Components
A tree has three main parts (fig. 1.1):

i) the root system,
ii) the stem or trunk,
iii) the crown.

The roots anchor the tree firmly into the ground and, via many small root hairs, absorb a dilute solution of water and mineral salts, known as 'sap' (see fig. 1.2).

The stem or trunk conducts sap from the roots, stores food, and supports the crown. Timber is cut from this part of the tree.

The crown consists of branches, twigs, and foliage (leaves). Branches and twigs are the lifelines supplying the leaves with sap.

Food process (fig. 1.3)
The leaves play the vital role of producing the tree's food. By absorbing daylight energy, via the green pigment (chlorophyll) in the leaf, they convert a mixture of carbon dioxide taken from the air and sap from the

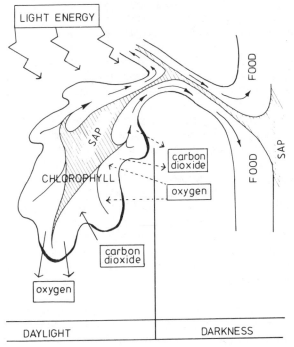

Fig. 1.3 The process of photosynthesis

3

roots into the necessary amounts of sugars and starches (referred to as 'food'), while at the same time releasing oxygen into the atmosphere as a waste product. This process is known as 'photosynthesis'. However, during the hours of darkness this action to some extent is reversed – the leaves take in oxygen and give off carbon dioxide, a process known as 'respiration' (breathing).

For the whole process to function, there must be some form of built-in system of circulation which allows sap to rise from the ground to the leaves and then to descend as food to be distributed throughout the whole tree. It would seem that this action is due either to suction induced by 'transpiration' (leaves giving off moisture by evaporation) and/or to capillarity (see section 12.2) within the cell structure of the wood.

Structural elements
The following features are illustrated in fig. 1.4.

Pith (medulla) – the core or centre of the tree, formed from the tree's earliest growth as a sapling.

Growth ring (sometimes referred to as an annual ring) – wood cells which have formed around the circumference of the tree during its growing season. The climate and time of year dictate the growth pattern. Each ring is often seen as two distinct bands, known as 'earlywood' (springwood) and 'latewood' (summerwood). Latewood is usually more dense than earlywood and can be recognised by its darker appearance.

Sapwood (alburnum) – the outer active part of the tree which, as its name implies, receives and conducts sap from the roots to the leaves. As this part of the tree matures, it gradually becomes heartwood.

Heartwood (duramen) – the natural non-active part of the tree, often darker in colour than sapwood, gives strength and support to the tree and provides the most durable wood for conversion into timber.

Rays – these all appear (although falsely) to originate from the centre (medulla) of the tree, hence the term 'medullary rays' is often used to describe this strip of cells that allow sap to percolate across the area of sapwood. They are also used to store excess food.

Rays are more noticeable in hardwood than in softwood (see section 1.2), and even then can be seen with the naked eye only in such woods as oak and beech. Figure 1.18 shows how rays may be used as a decorative feature once the wood has been converted (sawn into timber).

Cambium – a thin layer or sleeve of cells located between the sapwood and the bast (phloem). These cells are responsible for the tree's growth. As they are formed, they become subdivided in such a way that new cells are added to both sapwood and bast, thus increasing the girth of the tree.

4

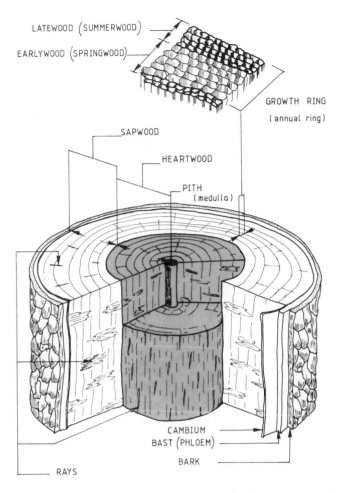

Fig. 1.4 Section through the stem/trunk

Bast (phloem) − conducts food throughout the whole of the tree, from the leaves to the roots.

Bark − the outer sheath of the tree. It functions as

a) a moisture barrier,
b) a thermal insulator,
c) an armour plate against extremes of temperature, attack by insects and fungi, and animals.

   The bark of a well established tree can usually withstand minor damage, although excessive ill treatment to this region could prove fatal.

1.2 Hardwoods and softwoods

The terms 'hardwood' and 'softwood' can be very confusing, as not all commercially classified hardwoods are physically hard, or softwoods soft. For example, the obeche tree is classed as a hardwood tree, yet it offers little resistance to a saw or chisel etc. The yew tree, on the other hand, is much harder to work yet it is classified as a softwood. To add to this confusion we could be led to believe that hardwood trees are deciduous (shed their leaves at the end of their growing season) and softwood trees are evergreen (retain their leaves for more than one year), which is true of most species within these groups, but not all!

Table 1.1 identifies certain characteristics found in hardwood and softwood trees; however, it should be used only as a general guide.

Table 1.1 Guide to the recognition of hardwoods and softwoods (see fig. 1.2)

	Hardwood	Softwood (conifers)
a) Botanical group	Angiosperms	Gymnosperms
b) Leaf growth	Deciduous and evergreen	Evergreen*
c) Leaf shape	Broadleaf	Needle leaf
d) Seed	Encased	Naked via cone
e) General use	Decorative; heavy structural	General structural

* Not always the case − e.g. larches

'Hardwood' and 'softwood' in fact refer to botanical differences in cell composition and structure. (Cell types and their formation are dealt with in volume 2.)

1.3 Sources and supply of timber

The forests of the world that supply the wood for timber, veneers, wood pulp, and chippings for particle board are usually situated in areas which are typical for a particular group of tree species. For example, the coniferous forests supplying the bulk of the world's softwoods are mainly found in the cooler regions of northern Europe, also Canada and Asia − stretching to the edge of the Arctic Circle. Hardwoods, however, come either from a temperate climate (neither very hot nor very cold) − where they are mixed with faster-growing softwoods − or from subtropical to tropical regions, where each continent seems to cater for different types.

Tree and timber names

Common names are often given to trees (and other plants) so as to include a group of similar yet botanically different species. It is these common English names which are predominantly used in the timber industry. The true name or Latin botanical name of the tree must be used where formal identification is required − for example:

Common English name	Species (true name or Latin botanical name)	
	Genus (generic name or 'surname')	Specific name (or 'forename')
Teak	Tectona	grandis

As a general guide, it could therefore be said that plants have both a surname and a forename and, to take it a step further, belong to family groups of hardwood and softwood.

Commercial names for timber often cover more than one species. In these cases, the botanical grouping is indicated by 'spp.'.

Softwoods

Most timber used in the UK for carpentry and joinery purposes is softwood imported from Sweden, Finland, and the USSR. The most important of these softwoods are European redwood (*Pinus sylvestris*), which includes Baltic redwood, and Scots pine, a native of the British Isles. As timber, these softwoods are collectively called simply 'redwood'. Redwood is closely followed in popularity by European whitewood, a group which includes Baltic whitewood and Norway spruce (*Picia abies*) – recognised the world over as the tree most commonly used at Christmas time. Commercially these and sometimes silver firs are simply referred to as 'whitewood'.

Larger growing softwoods are found in the Pacific coast region of the USA and Canada. These include such species as Douglas fir (*Pseudotsuga menziesii*) – known also as Columbian or Oregon pine, although technically not a pine – Western hemlock (*Tsuga heterophylla*), and Western red cedar (*Thuja plicata*), which is known for its durability, being almost immune from attack by insects or fungi. Brazil is the home of Parana pine (*Araucaria angustifolia*) which produces long lengths of virtually knot-free timber which is, however, only suitable for interior joinery purposes.

Temperate hardwoods

These hardwood trees are found where the climate is of a temperate nature. The temperate regions stretch into the northern hemisphere and south as far as Australia and New Zealand.

The United Kingdom is host to many of these trees, but not in sufficient quantities to meet all its needs. It must therefore rely on imports from countries which can provide such species as oak (*Quercus* spp.), sycamore (*Acer* spp.), ash (*Fraxinus* spp.), birch (*Betula* spp.), beech (*Fagus* spp.), and elm (*Ulmus* spp.) – which is now an endangered species due to Dutch elm disease.

7

Tropical and subtropical hardwoods

Most tropical hardwoods come from the rain forests of South America, Africa, and South East Asia. Listed below are some hardwoods which are commonly used:

African mahogany (*Khaya* spp.) − West Africa
Afrormosia (*Pericopsis elata*) − West Africa
Agba (*Gossweilerodendron balsamiferum*) − West Africa
American mahogany (Brazilian) (*Swietenia macrophylla*) − Central and South America
Gaboon (*Aucoumea klaineana*) − West Africa
Iroko (*Chlorophora excelsa*) − West Africa
Keruing (*Dipterocarpus* spp.) − South East Asia
Meranti (*Shorea* spp.) − South East Asia
Ramin (*Gonostylus* spp.) − South East Asia
Sapele (*Entandrophragma clindricum*) − West Africa
Teak (*Tectona grandis*) − Burma, Thailand
Utile (*Entandophragma utile*) − West Africa

Hardwood use

Hardwoods may be placed in one or more of the following groups:

Purpose group	Use
a) Decorative	Natural beauty − colour and/or figured grain
b) General-purpose	Joinery and light structural
c) Heavy structural	Withstanding heavy loads

Forms of supply

Softwood is usually exported from its country of origin as sawn timber in packages or in bundles. It has usually been pre-dried to about 20% m.c. (moisture content). Packaged timber is to a specified quality and size, bound or bonded with straps of steel or plastics for easy handling, and wrapped in paper or plastics sheets.

Hardwood, however, may be supplied as sawn boards or as logs to be converted (sawn) later by the timber importer to suit the customer's requirements.

1.4 Conversion

Felling (the act of cutting down a living tree) is carried out when trees are of a commercially suitable size, having reached maturity, or for thinning-out purposes. Once the tree has been felled, its branches will be removed, leaving the trunk in the form of a log. This log is the portion of the tree which is broken down by being sawn (converted) into timber − hence the term 'conversion'.

What, then, is the difference between 'wood' and 'timber'? The word 'wood' is often used very loosely to describe timber, when it should be used to describe either a collection of growing trees or the substance that

Fig. 1.5 'Forestor-150' horizontal band-mill − through-and-through sawing

trees are made of, i.e. the moisture-conducting cells and tissues etc. 'Timber' is wood in the form of squared boards or planks etc.

Initial conversion may be carried out in the forest, using heavy yet portable machines such as circular saws or vertical and horizontal band-mills (see fig. 1.5). In this way, transport is much reduced, as flat-sided sections can be more easily accommodated.

Alternatively, the logs may be transported by road, rail, or water to a permanently sited sawmill.

The type of sawing equipment used in a sawmill will depend on the size and kind of logs it handles; for example:

a) *Circular saw* (fig. 1.6) − small- to medium-diameter hardwoods and softwoods. Figure 1.6 shows a double-bladed circular saw being used to convert softwood logs in a Scandinavian sawmill.

b) *Vertical frame saw or gang saw* (fig. 1.7) − small- to medium-diameter softwoods. The log is fed and held in position by fluted rollers while being cut with a series of reciprocating (upward-and-downward moving) saw blades. The number and position of these blades will vary according to the size and shape of each timber section. Figure 1.8(a) illustrates the possible result after having passed the log through this machine once, whereas fig. 1.8(b) shows what could be achieved after making a further pass.

9

Fig. 1.6 Circular saw

Fig. 1.7 Frame saw

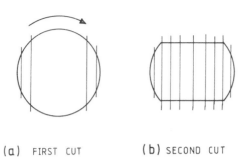

(a) FIRST CUT   (b) SECOND CUT

Fig. 1.8 Frame-saw cuts

Fig. 1.9 Band-mill capable of cutting logs up to 1.220 m diameter

c) *Vertical band-mill* (fig. 1.9) – all sizes of both hardwood and softwood. Logs are fed by a mechanised carriage to a saw blade in the form of an endless band which revolves around two large drums (pulleys), one of which is motorised. Figure 1.10 shows an example of how these cuts can be taken.

d) *Double vertical band-saw* (fig. 1.11) – small to medium logs. It has the advantage of making two cuts in one pass.

11

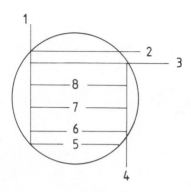

Fig. 1.10 Band-mill cuts

Fig. 1.11 Double vertical band-saw

e) *Horizontal band-saw* (fig. 1.5) – all sizes of hardwood and softwood. The machine illustrated is suitable for work at the forest site, or in a sawmill. Conversion is achieved by passing the whole mobile saw unit – which travels on rails – over a stationary log, taking a slice off at each forward pass.

The larger mills may employ a semi-computerised system of controls to their machinery, thus helping to cut down some human error and providing greater safety to the whole operation. The final control and decisions, however, are usually left to the expertise of the sawyer (machine operator).

Timber which requires further reduction in size is cut on a resaw machine. Figure 1.12 shows a resaw operation being carried out, and fig. 1.13 illustrates how two machines can be employed to speed up the operation.

Fig. 1.12 Resaw operation

Fig. 1.13 Band resaw in tandem arrangement

Importers of timber in the United Kingdom may specialise in either hardwoods or softwoods or both. Their sawmills will be geared to meet their particular needs, by resawing to customers' requirements. Hardwood specialists usually have their own drying facilities.

Timber sections

The way in which the log is cut (subdivided) will depend on the following factors:

a) cross-sectional area;
b) type of wood;
c) condition of the wood — structural defects etc. (see section 1.6);
d) proportion of heartwood to sapwood;
e) future use — structural, decorative, or both.

Broadly speaking, the measures taken to meet the customer's requirements will be the responsibility of the experienced sawyer (as mentioned earlier). His decisions will determine the method of conversion.

Through-and-through-sawn boards (fig. 1.14) In this method of conversion, parallel cuts are made down the length of the log, producing a number of 'radial' and 'tangential' sawn boards (figs 1.15 and 1.16). The first and last cuts leave a portion of wood called a 'slab'. This method of conversion is probably the simplest and least expensive.

SLAB

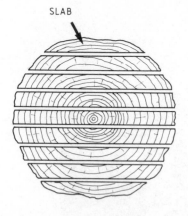

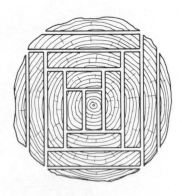

Fig. 1.14 Through-and-through (plain or flat) sawn

Fig. 1.15 Tangential sawn

Tangential-sawn boards (fig. 1.15) Starting with a squared log, tangential-sawn boards are produced by working round the log by turning it, to produce boards all of which (except the centre) have their growth rings across the boards' width. Although tangential-sawn sections are subject to cupping (becoming hollow across the width) when they dry, they are the most suitable sections for softwood beams, i.e. floor joists, roof rafters, etc., which rely on the position of the growth ring to give greater strength to the beam's depth.

Quarter (radial) or rift-sawn boards (fig. 1.16) This method of conversion can be wasteful and expensive, although it is necessary where a large number of radial or near radial-sawn boards are required. Certain hardwoods cut in this fashion produce beautiful figured boards, for example figured oak, as a result of the rays being exposed (fig. 1.4). Quarter-sawn boards retain their shape better than tangential-sawn boards and tend to shrink less, making them well suited to good-class joinery work and quality flooring.

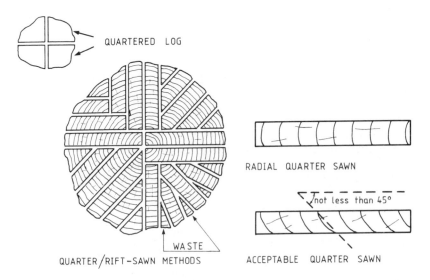

Fig. 1.16 Quarter sawn

Conversion geometry (fig. 1.17) Although a log's cross-section can be anything but circular, the above-mentioned saw cuts and sections can be related to a circle and its geometry. For example, timber sawn from a 'radius' line will be radial-sawn or quartered logs (divided by cutting into four quarters, or 'quadrants'). Similarly, any cut made as a tangent to a growth ring would be called 'tangential-sawn'. The chords are straight lines which start and finish at the circumference; therefore a series of chords can be related to a log which has been sawn 'through-and-through' or plain sawn. It should be noted that the chord line is also used when cuts are made tangential to a growth ring, and when the log is cut in half.

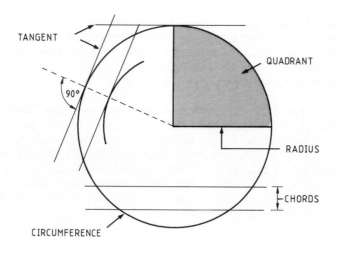

Fig. 1.17 Conversion geometry

Decorative-sawn boards Figure 1.18 gives two examples of how wood can be cut to produce timber with an attractive face.

The tangential-sawn softwood relies on the appearance of its growth rings, whereas the hardwood is quarter-sawn to show off its rays to great advantage.

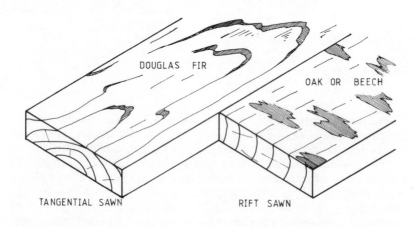

Fig. 1.18 Grain figuring

1.5 Size and selection of timber

Sawn timber is available in a wide variety of lengths, cross-sections, and species, to meet the different needs of the construction and building industry. Tables 1.2 and 1.3 show some of the standard sizes that can be made available through timber merchants. Figure 1.19 shows the sequence and method of ordering. The species, actual cross-section, length, quantity, and processing (or finish) should be quoted in that order.

By adopting standard sizes, we can reduce the time spent on further conversion, subsequent wastage, and the inevitable build-up of short ends or off-cuts ('off-cuts' usually refers to waste pieces of sheet materials), thereby making it possible to plan jobs more efficiently and economically.

A large part of our industry is made up of small joinery firms which, due to their size, do not always have the machinery or storage facilities to handle large quantities of timber. These firms rely on small timber merchants to provide a service whereby stock sizes of both sawn and planed timber (Table 1.4) are readily available.

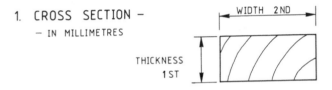

1. CROSS SECTION –
   – IN MILLIMETRES

   WIDTH 2ND

   THICKNESS 1ST

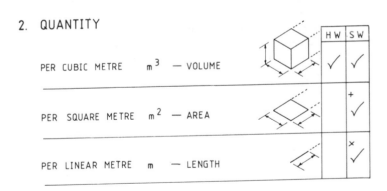

2. QUANTITY

		HW	SW
PER CUBIC METRE	m^3 — VOLUME	✓	✓
PER SQUARE METRE	m^2 — AREA		+ ✓
PER LINEAR METRE	m — LENGTH		× ✓

+ eg. FLOOR OR MATCHBOARD etc.

× eg. SMALL QUANTITIES

3. FINISH

   TYPE OF PROCESSING. (Fig. 1.20)

Fig. 1.19 Sequence and method of ordering

Table 1.2 Basic sizes of sawn softwood (all dimensions in mm)

a) Cross-sectional sizes

Thickness	Width								
	75	100	125	150	175	200	225	250	300
16	×	×	×	×					
19	×	×	×	×					
22	×	×	×	×					
25	×	×	×	×	×	×	×	×	×
32	×	×	×	×	×	×	×	×	×
36	×	×	×	×					
38	×	×	×	×	×	×	×		
44	×	×	×	×	×	×	×	×	×
47*	×	×	×	×	×	×	×	×	×
50	×	×	×	×	×	×	×	×	×
63		×	×	×	×	×	×		
75		×	×	×	×	×	×	×	×
100		×		×		×		×	×
150				×		×			×
200						×			
250								×	
300									×

* This range of widths for 47 mm thickness will usually be found to be available in constructional quality only.

Note The smaller sizes contained within the broken lines are normally but not exclusively of European origin. The larger sizes outside the dotted lines are normally but not exclusively of North and South American origin.

b) Lengths

1.80	2.10	3.00	4.20	5.10	6.00	7.20
	2.40	3.30	4.50	5.40	6.30	
	2.70	3.60	4.80	5.70	6.60	
		3.90			6.90	

Note Lengths of 6.00 m and over will generally only be available from North American species and may have to be recut from larger sizes.

Table 1.3 Basic sizes of sawn hardwood (all dimensions in mm)

a) Cross-sectional sizes

Thickness	Width										
	50	63	75	100	125	150	175	200	225	250	300
19			×	×	×	×	×				
25	×	×	×	×	×	×	×	×	×	×	×
32			×	×	×	×	×	×	×	×	×
38			×	×	×	×	×	×	×	×	×
50				×	×	×	×	×	×	×	×
63						×	×	×	×	×	×
75						×	×	×	×	×	×
100						×	×	×	×	×	×

Note Designers and users should check the availability of specified sizes in any particular species.

b) Lengths The basic lengths of hardwoods shall be any integral multiple of 100 mm, but not less than 1 m.

Note The normal length of imported hardwood will vary according to the species and the origin.

Table 1.4 Reductions of sawn softwood from basic size to finished size by planing of two opposed faces (all dimension in mm)

Purpose	Reductions from basic sizes			
	15 up to and including 35	Over 35 up to and including 100	Over 100 up to and including 150	Over 150
(a) Constructional timber	3	3	5	6
(b) Matching*; interlocking boards	4	4	6	6
(c) Wood trim not specified in BS 584	5	7	7	9
(d) Joinery and cabinet work	7	9	11	13

* The reduction of width is overall the extreme size and is exclusive of any reduction of the face by the machining of a tongue or lap joint.

Buying pre-planed or shaped timber adds considerably to the cost – further stressing the importance of selecting the correct standard stock sizes wherever possible.

Figure 1.20 shows how the sizes in Table 1.4 have been achieved, together with the planing sequence as follows:

a) EX – sawn to nominal size
b) S1S – surfaced one side   or   P1S – planed one side
c) S1S1E – surfaced one side and one edge   or   P1S1E – planed one side and one edge
d) S1S2E – surfaced one side and two edges   or   P1S2E – planed one side and two edges
e) S4S – surfaced four sides   or   P4S – planed four sides

p.a.r. – planed all round

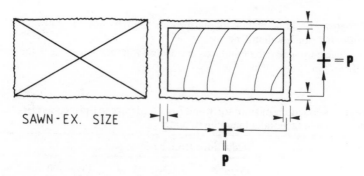

SAWN - EX. SIZE

P = 3 to 13mm DEPENDING ON BOARD WIDTH

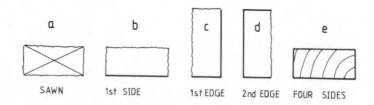

PLANING SEQUENCE

N.B. PLANED TIMBER IS QUOTED BY NOMINAL SIZE, i.e. SAWN SIZE.

Fig. 1.20 Machine planing

20

Being able to recognise a piece of timber by its common name can be just as important as ordering the correct amounts. Listed below is a selection of common-named timbers. By referring to sections 1.2 and 1.3, see if you can allocate them to their botanical classification, i.e. H.W. (hardwood) or S.W. (softwood).

	H.W.	S.W.
1. Afrormosia		
2. Balsa		
3. Beech		
4. Douglas fir (Columbian or Oregon pine)		
5. Elm		
6. Iroko		
7. Mahogany		
8. Oak		
9. Parana pine		
10. Scots pine (redwood)		
11. Spruce (whitewood)		
12. Sycamore		
13. Teak		
14. Western red cedar		
15. Western hemlock		
	9	6
Total	15	

[*Answers:* H.W. − 1, 2, 3, 5, 6, 7, 8, 12, 13; S.W. − 4, 9, 10, 11, 14, 15]

Common timbers are usually identified by recognising familiar characteristics, for example colour, weight, texture, and smell.

1.6 Structural defects (natural defects)

Figures 1.21 to 1.23 show defects that may be evident before and/or during conversion. Most of these defects have little, if any, detrimental effect on the tree, but they can degrade the timber cut from it, i.e. lower its market value.

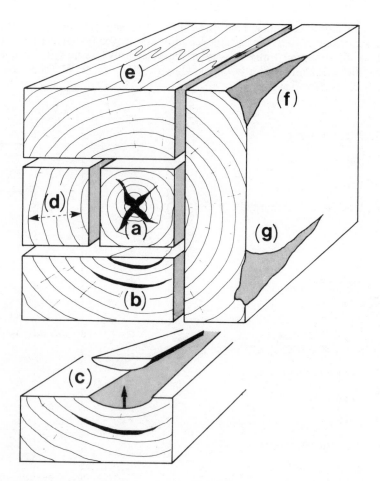

Fig. 1.21 Structural defects

Heart shake (fig. 1.21(a)) – shake (parting of wood fibres along the grain) within the heart (area around the pith) of the tree – caused by uneven stresses, which increase as the wood dries.

Star shake (fig. 1.21(a)) – a collection of shakes radiating from the heart.

Ring shake (cup shake) (fig. 1.21(b)) – a shake which follows the path of a growth ring. Figure 1.21(c) shows the effect it can have on a length of timber.

Rate of growth (fig. 1.21(d)) – the number of growth rings per 25 mm determines the strength of the timber.

Compression failure (upset) (fig. 1.21(e)) – fracturing of the fibres; thought to be caused by sudden shock, either during the tree's growth or at the time of felling. Found mainly in mahogany.

Wane (waney edge) (fig. 1.21(f)) – the edge of a piece of timber which has retained part of the tree's rounded surface.

Encased bark (fig. 1.21(g)) – may appear on the face or the edge of a piece of timber.

Sloping grain (fig. 1.22) – the grain (direction of the wood fibres) slopes in a way that can make load-bearing timbers unsafe, e.g. beams and joists.

Knots (fig. 1.23) – where the tree's branches have joined the stem and become an integral part of it. Figure 1.23 shows how knots may appear in the sawn timber. The size, type, location, and number of knots are controlling factors when the timber is graded for use.

Dead knots (fig. 1.23) If a branch is severely damaged, that part adjoining the stem will die and may eventually become enclosed as the tree develops – not being revealed until conversion into timber. Note: these knots are often loose, making them a potential hazard whenever machining operations are carried out.

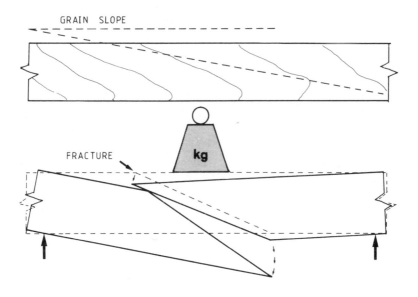

Fig. 1.22 Sloping grain – possible failure

23

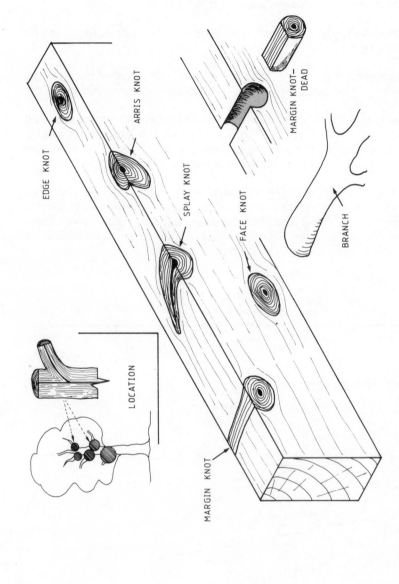

Fig. 1.23 Knot recognition — systems of knots

24

1.7 Seasoning and moisture content

Timber derived from freshly felled wood is said to be 'green', meaning that the cell cavities contain free moisture and the wall fibres are saturated (fig. 1.28), making the wood heavy, structurally weak, susceptible to attack by insects and/or fungi, and unworkable. Timber in this condition is therefore always unsuitable for use. The amount of moisture the wood contains as a percentage of the oven-dry weight is known as the 'moisture content' (m.c.), and the process of reducing the m.c. is termed 'seasoning'.

Seasoning, or drying, timber is usually carried out by one of three methods:

i) air seasoning (natural drying),
ii) kiln seasoning (artificial drying),
iii) air seasoning followed by kiln seasoning.

All three methods aim at producing timber that will remain stable in both size and shape – the overriding factor being the final moisture content, which ultimately controls the use of the timber. Some examples can be seen in fig. 1.24.

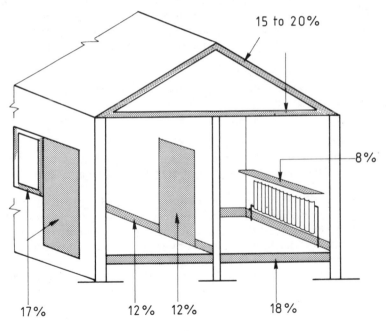

15 to 20%

8%

17%   12%   12%   18%

N.B. Wood with a 20% +M.C. is liable to attack by fungi.

Fig. 1.24 Moisture content of timber in various situations

Air seasoning

Air seasoning is carried out in open-sided sheds, where the timber is exposed to the combined action of circulating air and temperature, which lifts and drives away unwanted moisture by a process of evaporation (similar to the drying of clothes on a washing line). A suitable reduction in m.c. can take many months, depending on

a) the amount of exposure,
b) the type of wood (hardwood or softwood),
c) the particular species,
d) the cross-sectional size.

The final m.c. obtained can be as low as 16% to 17% in summer months and as high as 20% or more during winter. It would therefore be fair to say that this method of seasoning is very unreliable.

A typical arrangement for air seasoning is shown in fig. 1.25, where the features numbered are of prime importance if satisfactory results are to be achieved. They are as follows.

1. Timber stacks (piles of sawn timber) must always be raised off the floor, thus avoiding rising damp from the ground. Concrete, gravel, or ash will provide a suitable site covering.
2. The area surrounding the shed must be kept free from ground vegetation, to avoid conduction of moisture from the ground.
3. Free circulation of air must be maintained throughout the stack — the size and position of 'sticks' will depend on the type, species, and section of timber being dried.
4. The roof covering must be sound, to protect the stacks from adverse weather conditions.

Kiln seasoning

This method of seasoning timber speeds up the drying process from months to days and produces an accurate and uniform m.c. throughout the whole stack.

Seasoning kilns may vary in their construction and methods of raising heat, but the working principles remain the same — to provide fully controllable drying conditions that will meet the requirements of different timbers without 'degrading' them in any way. (Defects caused by drying are discussed in volume 2.)

These drying units must therefore be provided with means of producing

a) enough heat — to sustain the required drying temperature;
b) enough moisture — so that the correct level of humidity can be maintained;
c) enough air circulation — to carry away moisture and ensure even drying throughout the complete stack.

The medium most commonly used to satisfy requirements (a) and (b) is *steam*.

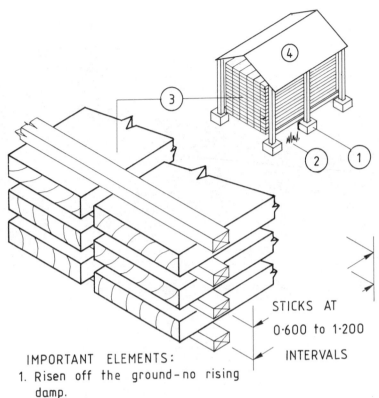

STICKS AT
0·600 to 1·200
INTERVALS

IMPORTANT ELEMENTS:
1. Risen off the ground – no rising damp.
2. Clear of ground vegetation.
3. Free circulation of air.
4. Protection from the weather.

Fig. 1.25 Air seasoning

Figure 1.26 shows a fully sticked stack of timber on its trolley, ready to be loaded in a kiln. The emission of vapour from the vents towards the top right-hand side of the picture indicates that the first two chambers are in operation. The cut-away section in fig. 1.27 shows a typical arrangement for circulating the air around the chamber, thus encouraging the evaporation of unwanted moisture from the wood and the subsequent drying process.

Moisture content
Figure 1.28 illustrates how moisture is lost and the effect on a timber section when it is present. If a timber section is to retain its desired m.c. after having gone through all the necessary drying stages, it must be kept in

27

Fig. 1.26 Typical loading of timber into a kiln

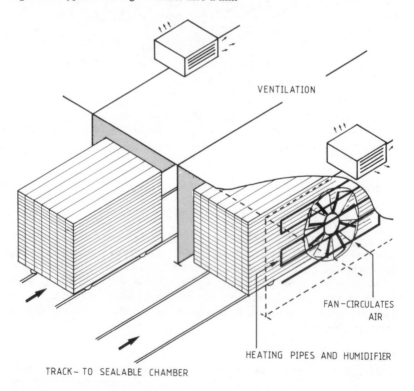

VENTILATION

FAN-CIRCULATES
AIR

HEATING PIPES AND HUMIDIFIER

TRACK- TO SEALABLE CHAMBER

Fig. 1.27 Kiln seasoning

28

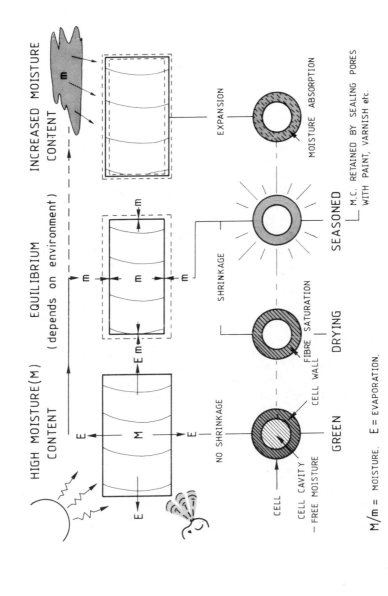

Fig. 1.28 Moisture movement

29

an environment conducive to its m.c. level, because wood is hygroscopic (having the ability to absorb moisture from the atmosphere). Any increase in moisture will result in the wood swelling.

It is, however, possible for timber in a changeable environment to remain stable if moisture absorption can be prevented. This can be achieved by one of two methods:

 i) completely sealing all its exposed surfaces;
ii) using a micro-pore sealer which prevents direct entry of water from outside but allows trapped moisture to escape.

All timber must of course be fully seasoned before the above treatments are carried out.

Shrinkage
The loss of moisture from the wood during the seasoning process should now be understood. However, this loss of moisture can have quite an adverse effect on the size and shape of the timber.

The proportion of movement (shrinkage) that takes place is shown in fig. 1.29, where it will be seen that the greatest amount of movement takes place tangentially, that is to say in the direction of each growth ring. Radial shrinkage accounts for about half that amount, whereas shrinkage along the length of the grain will be least of all. By relating fig. 1.29(a) to fig. 1.29(d), it should be possible to see why and how timber sections become distorted when dried.

Figure 1.30 gives examples of how different cuts from the log become affected by shrinkage.

1.8 Common enemies
If its condition is favourable, most wood can be attacked by fungi or wood-boring beetles or both. Such attacks are often responsible for the destruction of many of our trees (e.g. Dutch elm disease) and for the decomposition and subsequent failure of many timbers commonly used in building.

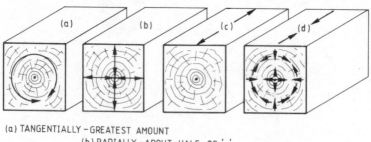

(a) TANGENTIALLY – GREATEST AMOUNT
(b) RADIALLY – ABOUT HALF OF 'a'
(c) LENGTH – LEAST AMOUNT
(d) OVERALL SHRINKAGE

Fig. 1.29 Proportion of wood shrinkage

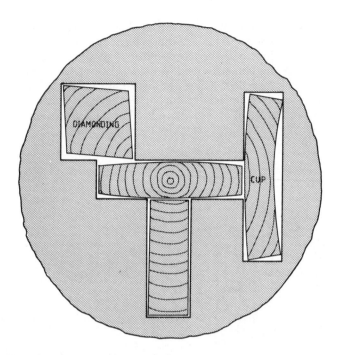

Fig. 1.30 Shrinkage – its effect on timber

Fungi
There are many different types and species of fungi, all belonging to the
plant kingdom. The fungi that concern us are those that take their food
from and live on or in growing trees and the timber cut from them.

'Sap-staining' fungi, often known as 'blue-stain' or 'blueing' fungi,
obtain their nourishment from the cell contents of sapwood, leaving the
cell walls unscathed; therefore the only degrading effect these fungi have
on wood is the bluish discolouration they leave. They only attack wood
with a high m.c.; so, to prevent attacks by these fungi, it is necessary that
conversion and seasoning are carried out as early as possible after the trees
have been felled.

However, the wood-destroying types of fungi are a different matter, as
they live off the cell walls of the wood, thus causing its whole structure to
decompose and eventually collapse. Their growth requirements are simply
wood with above 20% m.c. for their initial germination and subsequent
nourishment in the form of non-durable sapwood.

Durable timbers are those which have a natural resistance to fungal
attack; however, the majority of timbers have either to be kept
permanently below 20% m.c. or to undergo treatment with a suitable
wood preservative, as an assurance against attack.

All wood-destroying fungi have a similar life cycle, and a typical example is shown in fig. 1.31. The spores have been transported from the parent plant (fruiting body or sporophore) — by wind, insects, animals, or an unsuspecting human — to a suitable piece of fertile wood where germination can take place. Once established, the fungus spreads its roots (hyphae) — which are in fact the body of the fungus — into and along the wood in search of food, eventually to become a mass of tubular threads which collectively are called 'mycelium', which will produce a fruiting body.

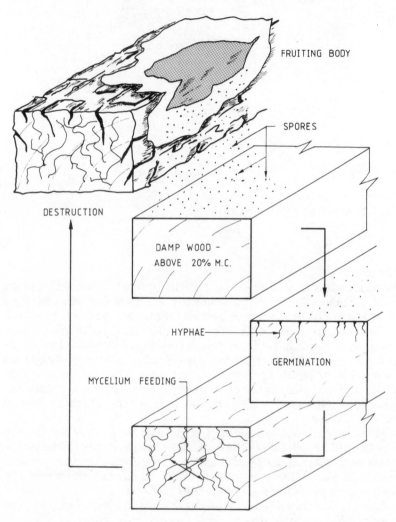

Fig. 1.31 Process of wood-destroying fungi

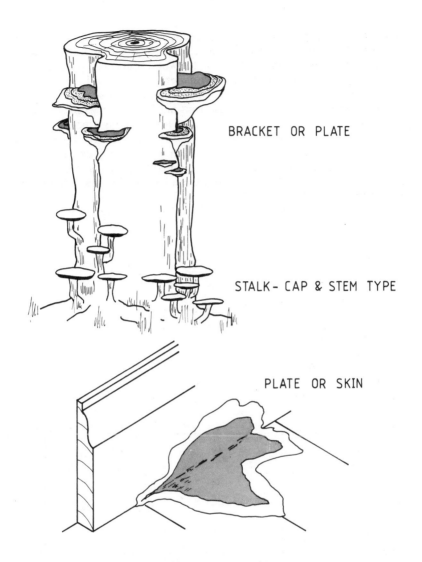

BRACKET OR PLATE

STALK- CAP & STEM TYPE

PLATE OR SKIN

Fig. 1.32 Fruiting bodies (sporophores)

Fruiting bodies (sporophores) take the shape of stalks, brackets, or plates etc. (fig. 1.32), depending on the species of fungus. Each fruiting body is capable of producing and shedding millions of minute spores, of which only a very small proportion will germinate.

Wood-boring beetles
The term 'wood-boring beetle' as opposed to 'woodworm' can be confusing. Although this beetle is capable of biting holes into wood, it is

the larva or grub (woodworm) of the beetle which is directly responsible for the damage done to the wood. Damage is brought about by the endless tunnelling of the larva while it feeds on the wood substance. It is therefore inevitable that wherever mass infestation is present there will always be the danger that the whole of the wood structure may collapse.

There are many varieties of wood-boring beetle — each with its own life style. For example, there are those which attack living trees, or which prefer trees which have been recently felled, while others only attack certain species — and there are those which are not too particular.

Probably the best known beetle in the United Kingdom is the 'common furniture beetle'. Evidence of its attack can be found in many homes, in both furniture and structural members, where it devours hardwood, softwood, and plywood alike, although it does tend to prefer the sapwood first.

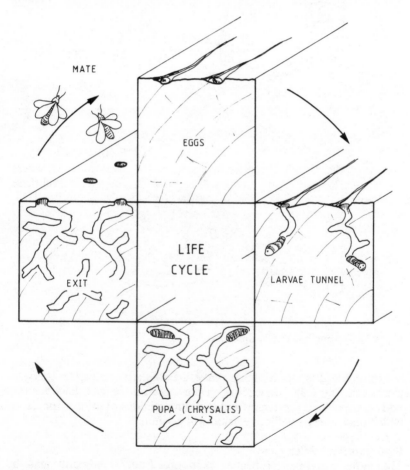

Fig. 1.33 Life cycle of a wood-boring beetle

Figure 1.33 represents a typical life cycle of a wood-destroying beetle:

i) Eggs will be laid by the female beetle in small cavities below the surface of the wood.

ii) After a short period (usually a few weeks) the eggs hatch into larvae (grubs) and enter the wood, where they progressively gnaw their way further into the wood, leaving excreted wood dust (frass) in the tunnel as they move along.

iii) After one or more years of tunnelling (depending on the species of beetle) the larva undermines a small chamber just below the surface of the wood, where it pupates (turns into a chrysalis).

iv) The 'pupa' then takes the form of a beetle and emerges from its chamber by biting its way out, leaving a hole known as an 'exit' or 'flight' hole. (Collectively, these holes are usually the first sign of any insect attack.) The insect is now free to travel or fly at will – to mate and complete its life cycle.

Wood-destroying beetles can often be identified by one or more of the following characteristics:

a) habitat,
b) size and shape of the beetle,
c) size and shape of the larva,
d) size and shape of the frass,
e) size and shape of the flight holes,
f) sound.

Probably the best preventative measure against insect attack is, where practicable, to keep the m.c. of wood below 10%, for at this level these insects will be discouraged from breeding. As can be seen from fig. 1.24, most structural timber members of a building exceed this m.c., therefore if the building has a history of insect attack or is sited in a geographical area where infestation is common (as is the case in certain areas in the United Kingdom) then suitable preservative methods should be considered.

Preventative and remedial treatment for outbreaks of both fungal and insect attack are dealt with in volume 2.

1.9 Manufactured boards

We have seen how wood can be subject to dimensional change and distortion when used in its solid state. It is this inherent problem, together with its cost, that often restricts the use of wood where wide or large areas have to be covered. This is the kind of work where manufactured boards are mainly used.

For the purpose of this chapter, 'manufactured boards' will be taken to mean those sheet materials which for their greater part are composed of wood veneer, strips, particles, or their combination. They fall into the following groups:

a) plywood (including laminboard, blockboard, and battenboard);
b) particle board;
c) fibre board.

Plywood (fig. 1.34)
The word 'plywood' is usually taken to refer to those sheets or boards which are made from three or more odd numbers of thin layers of wood — known as wood 'veneers'. It is important that all veneers on each side of the core or centre veneer are balanced (see fig. 1.42).

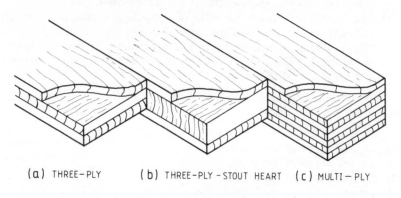

(a) THREE−PLY   (b) THREE−PLY −STOUT HEART   (c) MULTI−PLY

NOTE − AN <u>ODD</u> NUMBER OF VENEERS

Fig. 1.34 Plywood

Three ply (fig. 1.34(a)) consists of a face and back veneer (ply) sandwiching either a central veneer of the same thickness or a core of thicker veneer, usually of a lesser density (fig. 1.34(b)).

Multi-ply (fig. 1.34(c)) — the face, core, and backing consist of more than three plies, usually of a similar thickness.

Plywood veneers are usually produced by peeling a log (fig. 1.35). The logs are cut to length, debarked, and (depending on the species) often steamed or given a similar treatment to soften the wood fibres before being peeled along their length. The resulting veneers are then cut to length, dried, and (depending on the thickness and number of plys required) glued together with the grain directions of alternate veneers running at right angles to one another. They are then pressed, cured, dried, trimmed to size, and finally dressed by sanding.

The type of glue used to bond the veneers together classifies the plywood with regard to its type and general use, as shown in Table 1.5.

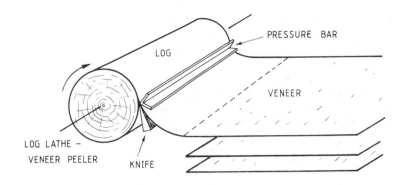

Fig. 1.35 Rotary veneer cutting

Table 1.5 Plywood adhesives and use

Adhesive type (bonding agent)	Plywood type	Use
INT	Interior use only	Not to be subjected to dampness
MR	Moisture-resistant	General use
CBR	Cyclical boil-resistant	Will not withstand extreme weather conditions
WBP	Weather- and boil-proof	Exterior quality

Although the adhesives used to bond the veneers control the plywood's use, the quality and final grade of the plywood is usually determined by the condition of the outer veneers, i.e. the presence of blemishes and knot holes etc., and the durability rating of the veneers.

Uses of plywood Depending on type and quality, plywood is used in a variety of ways, for example as

a) formwork,
b) roof decking,
c) flooring,
d) sheathing (covering the walls of timber-framed houses),
e) cladding,
f) wall panelling,
g) ceilings,
h) door panels,
i) carcassing (or frameworks),
j) shelving.

Laminboard (fig. 1.36)   This has a core made up of a lamination of narrow wood strips – not exceeding 7 mm wide – glued together, then faced with one or two veneers on each face. Laminboard has a virtually distortion-free surface.

Blockboard (fig. 1.37)   This is similar to laminboard, except that the wood strips used in its core are wider – usually between 19 mm and 28 mm. The board's finished surface is often slightly rippled.

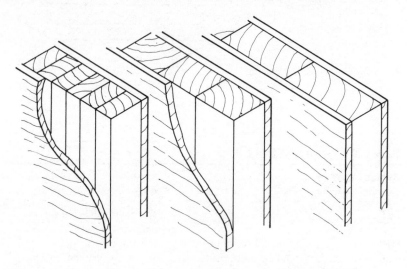

Fig. 1.36 Laminboard   **Fig. 1.37** Blockboard   **Fig. 1.38** Battenboard (obsolete)

Battenboard (fig. 1.38)   The only significant difference here is that the core material is much wider. It therefore follows that this type of board will be less stable than the others, and subject to more irregularities.

Battenboard is now obsolete and therefore not often seen in the United Kingdom.

Uses of laminated boards   The use of laminated boards is restricted to those areas which are not subjected to dampness, as most of these boards are bonded together with 'INT' types of adhesives.

Particle board (fig. 1.39)

The main natural ingredients which go to make particle board are wood chippings; hence the common name of 'chipboard'.

Wood required to produce these chippings comes from many different sources:

a) young trees,
b) forest thinnings,
c) slabs from sawmills (fig. 1.14),
d) wood-machining waste – shavings, chippings, etc.

Fibres from the flax plant also provide valuable raw material for particle-board production.

In simple terms, the manufacturing process involves the shredding of the raw material; drying and mixing it with a suitable synthetic-resin adhesive; and then, with the exception of 'extruded' boards, the substance is pressed flat between platens of a hot press, trimmed to size, and allowed to mature; then finally finished by sanding.

There are several types of these pressed boards, such as

  i) single-layer,
 ii) three-layer,
iii) graded-density.

Single-layer boards (fig. 1.39(a)) – a uniform mass of particles of either wood, flax, or both. The type, grade, and compaction of these particles will affect the board's strength and working properties – boards may for instance be classed as interior structural with regard to their use.

Because of their composition (uniformity of particles), single-layer boards present very few problems when being cut.

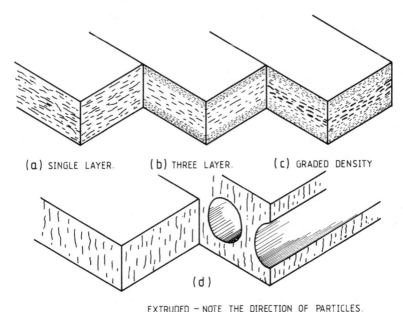

(a) SINGLE LAYER.   (b) THREE LAYER.   (c) GRADED DENSITY

(d)

EXTRUDED – NOTE THE DIRECTION OF PARTICLES.

Fig. 1.39 Particle board

Three-layer boards (fig. 1.39(b)) – these consist of a low-density core of large particles, sandwiched between two relatively higher-density layers of fine particles. These boards have a very smooth even surface suitable for direct painting etc. They may be classed as general-purpose or as interior non-structural.

Care should be taken when cutting these boards, as, unlike single-layer types, they are inclined to split or chip away at the cut edge.

Graded-density boards (fig. 1.39(c)) – these have a board structure midway between the single-layer and three-layer types. Their particles vary in size, getting smaller from the centre outwards. They are suitable for non-structural use and for furniture production.

Extruded boards (fig. 1.39(d)) – the prepared mixture of shredded chippings and adhesive passes through a die, resulting in an extruded board of predetermined thickness and width but of unlimited length. The holes in these boards are made by metal heating tubes, which assist in curing the adhesive, thus enabling much thicker boards to be produced. These holes also reduce the overall weight of the board.

Chipboard produced in this way will have some of its particles located at right angles to the face of the board, thus reducing its strength. However, the main use of these boards is as comparatively lightweight core material to be sandwiched between suitable layers of veneers or other materials to give it the required stability.

Uses of chipboard   Chipboard generally can be used in situations similar to plywood. Its use is however determined by

a) its method of manufacture,
b) the bonding agent,
c) special treatment – surface (e.g. laminates) or integral (e.g. fire retardants).

BS 5669 defines four grades of chipboard for particular uses:

Type I – general-purpose, e.g. furniture production.
Type II – general domestic flooring grade (decking) with impact-resistance requirement.
Type III – improved resistance to the effects of moisture.
Type II/III – combines strength with resistance to impact and moisture.

Wood–cement particleboard   A mixture of wood particles and cement, producing a high-density board. Used where fire and weather resistance are required, for example.

Waferboard   Wafers of wood, approximately 75 mm × 75 mm and 4 to 6 mm thick, randomly arranged and glued together.

OSB (oriented strand board)   Narrower particles than waferboard, and more or less aligned. Boards are usually assembled in three layers – surface and core layers are oriented approximately at right angles.

Fibre board (fig. 1.40)
Fibre building boards are produced from wood which has been shredded into a fibrous state and then reassembled into a uniform sheet form.

The wood is first broken down into small chips then steam-treated to soften the lignin (natural resin) which binds the fibres together. Water is added to produce a wood pulp which is spread on to a slow-moving board-forming machine (see fig. 1.40), where it is rolled out to a uniform thickness (most of the water has been removed before this operation). What follows will depend on the required density of the finished board.

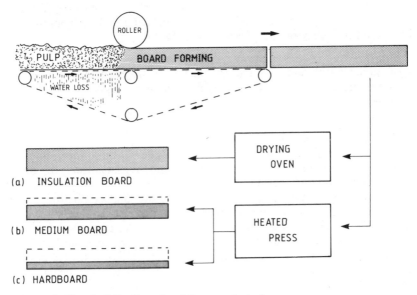

Fig. 1.40 Fibre building board and its manufacturing process

Softboard is a low density non-compressed board which has been dried in an oven. Its cellular core is the result of moisture having evaporated during its drying process and gives the board good insulation properties – hence its name 'insulation board'. Medium board and hardboard are compressed between heated presses to a density suitable for their use.

Insulation board – softboard (fig. 1.40(a)) – a lightweight board available in sheet or tile form, with surfaces which are flat, grooved, patterned, or with stopped holes etc. Used on ceiling, walls, and floors.

Medium board – three types of mid-density boards between insulation board and hardboard):

i) Type LM (fig. 1.40(b)) – low-density board. Used for display and notice boards etc. – drawing pins can easily enter the board.
ii) Type HM (fig. 1.40(b)) – panel board – higher density than LM. Used for wall lining, partitions, etc.
iii) Type MDF (medium-density fibreboard) – made by a 'dry' process with resin binders. Used for furniture, decorative mouldings, frames for flush doors, etc.

Hardboard (fig. 1.40(c)) – a high-density sheet material with one smooth face. An ideal panel and lining material, often used as a cheaper alternative to plywood. Available with an enamelled or lacquered surface, or with a patterned or textured finish. Perforated boards (pegboard) can be used for display or as a means of ventilation.

Tempered hardboard – standard hardboard impregnated with oil or resin to increase its strength and water resistance, making it suitable for exterior use.

1.10 Laminated plastics
Laminated plastics are thin synthetic (man-made) plastics veneers and are capable of providing a both decorative and hygienic finish to most horizontal and vertical surfaces.

Figure 1.41 shows how the laminations are built-up before being bonded together by a combination of heat and pressure.

The finished sheets are usually supplied in large sheet sizes, but, because of their thickness, (not usually more than 1.5 mm) and their hard surface, handling can prove difficult, for they are liable to split or shatter if they are subjected to sharp or sudden bends or blows, some types being more brittle than others.

Because of their flimsy nature, these sheets are best stored flat (face to face), otherwise they will be inclined to take on and retain the shape that they are left in, i.e. bent, bowed, twisted, etc. A further precaution when storing is to ensure that no grit is trapped between the sheets' decorative surfaces, otherwise, as one sheet is drawn over the other, the chances are that its surface will be permanently scratched.

Cutting and trimming
The veneers can be cut successfully by using hand and/or machine tools.

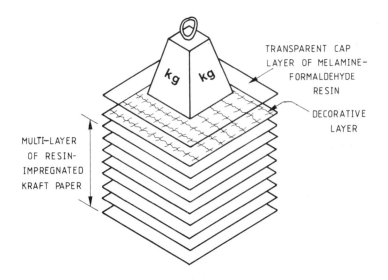

Fig. 1.41 Laminated plastics – its composition

Hand tools Cutting can be carried out by using either a sharp fine-toothed tenon saw, cutting from the decorative face, or by scoring through the decorative face with a purpose-made scoring tool then gently lifting the waste or off-cut side, thus closing the V and allowing the sheet to break along the scored line.

A block plane and/or file can be used to trim edges. Always remember to keep your hands and fingers away from these edges while this process is being carried out – processed edges can be very sharp.

Machine tools Because of its hard and brittle nature, special care must be taken both with regard to the method of holding laminated-plastics material while it is being cut and during the machining process.

Special blades and cutters (carbide-tipped) are available and are advisable for processing this material. While processing operations are being carried out there is always the risk of injury to the eyes. It is therefore essential that eye protection be worn, not only by the operator but also by others in close proximity to the operation.

Veneer application (fig. 1.42)
Because laminated plastics are used as veneers, their application on to board materials should be dealt with in a similar manner to that of a wood veneer; that is to say, if the backing board is to retain its shape, i.e. flatness, it must be kept in balance, therefore any veneer or additional veneers (in the case of plywood) applied to one face (fig. 1.42(a)) should have an equivalent compensating veneer applied to the opposite face

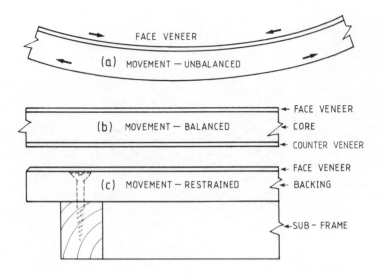

Fig. 1.42 Veneering

Table 1.6 Manufactured board and sheet-material sizes

Sheet material	Length(s) (mm)	Width(s) (mm)	Thickness (mm)
Plywood	Combination of the following sizes: 3050, 2745, 2440, 2135, 1830, 1525, 1270, 1220, 915 × 1830, 1525, 1270, 1220, 915		3 to 30
Laminboard and blockboard	1220 1830 2440	1220 2440 5105	12 to 38
Particle board (chipboard)	2440 3660 4575	610 1220	2 to 50
Hardboard	1220, 1830, 2440, 3660, up to 5490	610 1220	2 to 12
Medium board	1830 to 3660	1220	6 to 22
Insulation board	1830 2440 3050 3660	1220	9 to 25
Laminated plastics	2135 2440 3050 3660	915 1220 1525	0.8 to 1.5

(fig. 1.42(b)). In the case of laminated plastics, balancing or counter veneers are usually without a decorative finish, making them less expensive. An alternative to using a counter veneer is to secure the whole of the underside of the board to an under-frame or sub-frame (fig. 1.42(c)).

1.11 Board and sheet sizes

Table 1.6 gives some indication of the many board and sheet sizes available at timber merchants. It may be found, however, that future sheet sizes could follow a pattern of co-ordinating a few standard sizes; for example

Width (mm): 600, 900, 1200
Length (mm): 1800, 2400, 2700, 3000
Sample sheet size: say 1200 mm × 2400 mm or 1200 mm × 3000 mm

and so on.

1.12 Adhesives

Adhesives are made from either natural or synthetic materials. Table 1.7 lists six of these adhesives, together with some of their general characteristics. The following notes briefly describe these adhesives and some common terminology associated with them.

Adhesive type

Casein Derived from soured milk curds, which are dried, treated, and mixed with chemicals to produce a powder which, when mixed with water, is ready for use. It is used in general joinery assembly work and in the manufacture of plywood. It tends to stain some woods.

Urea formaldehyde (UF) A synthetic-resin adhesive, chemically cured (hardened) and available as a single- or two-part (two-component) adhesive. It is used for assembly work, veneering, and in the manufacture of plywood and particle board.

Resorcinol formaldehyde (RF) Composition similar to UF. A two-part adhesive used for outdoor timber structures.

Phenol formaldehyde (PF) Components similar to RF. Used in the manufacture of plywood and particle board.

Polyvinyl acetate (PVA) A thermoplastic adhesive, cured mainly by evaporation. PVA is a simple-to-use one-part emulsion type of adhesive, used extensively for glueing joinery components and veneering. This type of adhesive has been responsible for the dramatic decline in use of the once most popular joinery adhesive of all − animal glue, which was derived from animal bones and skins.

Table 1.7 Adhesive characteristics

	Adhesive type and classification	Moisture resistance	Single		Double		Gap filling			Bond pressure		General use
			PD	LQ	PD/LQ	LQ/LQ	Yes	MB	No	L	H	
N	Casein	–	Poor	√					√		√	√	Assembly work, plywood mnf.
SR	Urea formaldehyde (UF)	MR	Fair	√		√	√	√	√		√	√	Assembly work, veneering, plywood mnf., particle-board mnf.
SR	Resorcinol formaldehyde (RF)	WBP	Good			√	√	√			√		Outdoor timber structures
SR	Phenol formaldehyde (PF)	WBP	Good			√				√		√	Plywood mnf., particle-board mnf.
SR	Polyvinyl acetate (PVA)	–	Poor		√					√	√		Assembly work, veneering
N&S	Contact	–	Fair		√*					√	√		Veneering, laminated plastics

* Available in 'gel' form

Key: N – natural   SR – synthetic resin   N&S – natural and synthetic   PD – powder   LQ – liquid   MR – moisture-resistant   WBP – weather- and boil-proof   MB – maybe   L – low   H – high   mnf. – manufacture

Contact adhesives Adhesives made of natural or synthetic rubber and a solvent which evaporates when exposed to the air, giving off a heavy flammable vapour. These adhesives are used in the application of laminated plastics − bonding is achieved by coating both surfaces to be joined, leaving them to become tacky (for a time specified by the manufacturer), then laying one on to the other without trapping any air under the surfaces. Bonding is instantaneous on contact (hence the name 'contact' adhesive), with the exception of 'thixotropic' types which allow a certain amount of movement for minor adjustments.

Adhesive characteristics

Form Adhesives may be of the one- or two-component types − liquid, powder, or both. Two-component types become usable either by applying them direct from their containers, mixing their components together, or by applying each of their parts separately to the surfaces being joined. Some types, however, simply have to be mixed with water.

Moisture resistance This refers to the adhesive's inherent ability to resist decomposition by moisture. Resistance is classified in the following manner:

  MR − moisture-resistant,
  BR − boil-resistant,
  WBP − weather- and boil-proof,

to which reference has been made in section 1.9 with regard to the bonding of plywood veneers.

Gap filling Adhesives which qualify as gap-filling adhesives should be capable of spanning a 1.3 mm gap without crazing. They are used in situations where a tight fit cannot be assured.

Bond pressure This refers to the pressure necessary to ensure a suitable bond between the two or more surfaces joined together. The means by which pressure is applied is usually by either mechanical or manual presses or by clamps of various shapes and sizes. Wood wedges can be used not only to apply pressure but also to retain it permanently. The length of time needed to secure a bond will vary with each type of adhesive, its condition, and the surrounding temperature.

Storage life This is the stated time that the containerised adhesive will remain stable − beyond this period, marked deterioration may occur, affecting the strength and setting qualities.

Shelf life Once the adhesive's components have been exposed to the atmosphere, the storage life will usually be shortened. Shelf life therefore may or may not refer to the usable period after the initial opening — always note manufacturers' recommendations.

Pot life This is the length of time allowed for the adhesive to start to harden after either mixing or preparing the adhesive for use. (Note: working or assembly times can be taken as the time needed for hardening once the adhesive has been applied or spread on to the workpiece.)

Application of adhesives

Methods and equipment used in applying adhesives will depend on the following factors:

a) type of adhesive,
b) width of surface to be covered,
c) total surface area,
d) work situation,
e) clamping facilities,
f) quantity of work.

The spreading equipment in question could therefore be any one of the devices listed below:

 i) mechanical spreader,
 ii) roller,
iii) brush,
iv) spatula,
 v) toothed scraper.

Caution

All forms of adhesives should be regarded as being potentially hazardous if they are not used in accordance with the manufacturer's instructions — either displayed on the container or issued as a separate information sheet. Depending on the type of adhesive being used, failure to carry out the precautions thought necessary by the manufacturer could result in

a) an explosion — due to the adhesive's flammable nature or flammable vapour given off by it;
b) poisoning — due to inhaling toxic fumes or powdered components;
c) skin disorders (dermatitis) — due to contact while mixing or handling uncured adhesives — *always cover skin abrasions before starting work.*
   Where there is a risk of dermatitis, use a barrier cream or disposable protective gloves.
   Always wash hands thoroughly with soap and water at the end of a working period.

48

2 Hand tools and workshop procedures

2.1 Measuring tools

Measuring tools are used either to transfer measurements from one item to another or for checking pre-stated sizes.

Scale rule

At some stage in your career you will have to take sizes from or enter sizes on to a drawing – you must therefore familiarise yourself with methods of enlarging or reducing measurements accordingly. It is essential to remember that all sizes stated and labelled on working drawings will be true full sizes, but for practical reasons these sizes will in some cases have to be proportionally reduced to suit various paper sizes, by using one of the following scales: 1:2 (half full size), 1:5, 1:10, 1:20, 1:50, 1:100, 1:200, 1:1250, 1:2500.

Figure 2.1 illustrates the use of a scale rule, which enables lengths measured on a drawing to be converted to full-size measurements and vice versa.

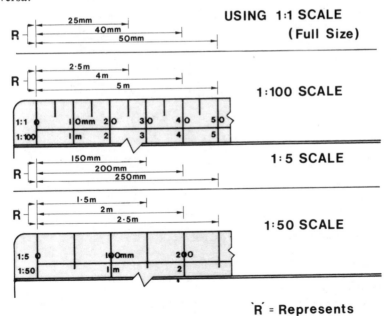

Fig. 2.1 Using a scale rule

Four-fold metre rule

This rule should have top priority on your list of tools. Not only is it capable of accurate measurement, it is also very adaptable (see fig. 2.2). It is available in both plastics and wood, and calibrated in both imperial and metric units. Some models (clinometer rules) also incorporate in their design a spirit-level and a circle of degrees from 0 to 180°.

With care, these rules will last for many years. It is therefore important when choosing one to find the type and make that suits your hand. Ideally, the rule should be kept about your person while at work. The most suitable

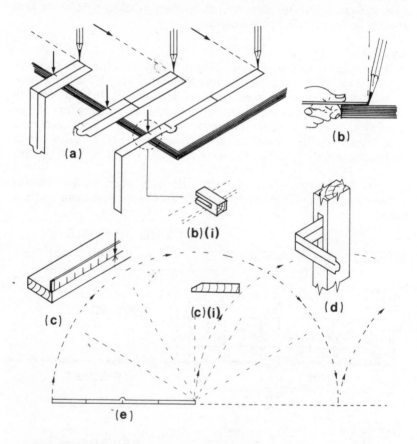

Fig. 2.2 The versatility of a four-fold metre rule:
a) ruling different widths
b) standard method of holding rule at (a)
b) (i) ruling aid − prevents cut fingers and splinters
c) transfering measurements
c) (i) chamfered edge − provides accurate flat reading
d) rule used as a depth gauge
e) stepping − measurements over 1m (approximate)

place is usually in a rule slide pocket sewn to the trouser leg of a bib and brace or overall etc. The use of a seat or back pocket is not a good idea.

Flexible steel tapes (fig. 2.3)
These tapes retract on to a small enclosed spring-loaded drum and are pulled out and either pushed back in or have an automatic return which can be stopped at any distance within the limit of the tape's length. Their overall length can vary from 2 m to 5 m, and they usually remain semi-rigid for about the first 500 mm of their length. This type of tool is an invaluable asset, particularly when involved in site work, as it fits easily in the pocket or clips over the belt.

It seems to have become common practice of late to use a tape as a substitute for a metre folding rule, though it is better used to complement it.

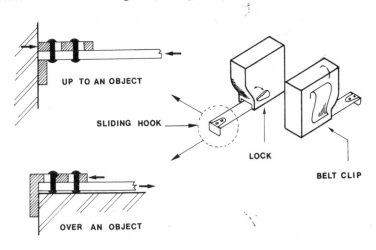

Fig. 2.3 Flexible steel tapes

2.2 Setting-out and marking-out tools

The drawings produced by the designer of a piece of work are usually reduced to an appropriate scale (fig. 2.1) so that an overall picture may be presented to the client. Once approval has been given, the setting-out programme can begin. This will involve redrawing various full-size sections through all the components necessary for the construction, to enable the joiner to visualise all the joint details etc. and make any adjustments to section sizes.

Setting-out is done on what is known as a 'rod'. A rod may be a sheet of paper, hardboard, or plywood, or a board of timber. By adopting a standard setting-out procedure, it is possible to simplify this process; for example (see fig. 2.4):

51

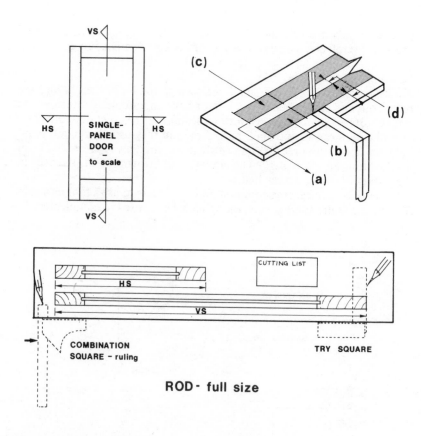

Fig. 2.4 Setting-out on a rod

i) draw all sections with their face side towards you (fig. 2.4(a));
ii) draw vertical sections (V.S.) first – with their tops to your left (fig. 2.4(b));
iii) draw horizontal sections (H.S.) above V.S. – keeping members with identical sections in line on H.S. and V.S., e.g. top rail with stile in fig. 2.4(c));
iv) allow a minimum of 20 mm between sections (fig. 2.4(d));
v) dimension only overall heights, widths, and depths.

Setting-out will involve the use of some, if not all, of the following tools and equipment:

a) a scale rule (fig. 2.1);
b) a straight-edge;
c) a four-fold metre rule (fig. 2.2);
d) drafting tape, drawing-board clips, or drawing pins;
e) an HB pencil;

f) a try-square (figs 2.4 and 2.9);
g) a combination square (figs 2.4 and 2.9);
h) dividers (fig. 2.5);
i) compasses (fig. 2.5);
j) a trammel (fig. 2.6).

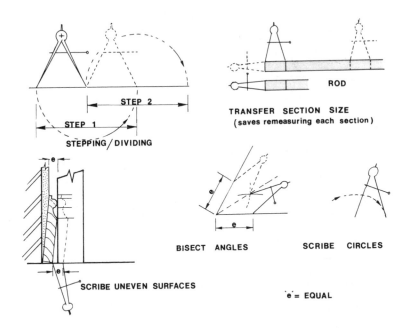

Fig. 2.5 Using dividers or compasses

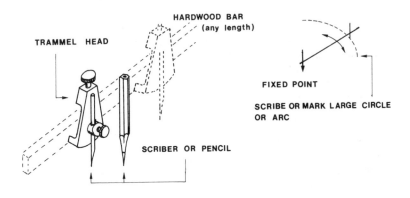

Fig. 2.6 Trammel

Figure 2.4 shows a space left on the rod for a cutting list. This is an itemised list of all the material sizes required to complete a piece of work. A typical cutting list is shown in fig. 2.7, together with provision for ironmongery etc. It follows that the information with regard to timber sizes and quantity will be required by the wood machinist (chapter 4).

JOB TITLE							JOB N°
QUANTITY		SAWN SIZE (EX.)			FINISH SIZE		
N°	ITEM	L	W	T	W	T	REMARKS

SUNDRIES – NAILS, SCREWS, HARDWARE, etc.	
QUANTITY	DESCRIPTION

L = Length   W = Width   T = Thickness

Fig. 2.7 Cutting and ironmongery list

Marking-out or marking-off involves the transfer of rod dimensions on to the pieces of timber and/or other materials needed. Provided that the rod is correct (double check), its use (see fig. 2.8) reduces the risk of duplicating errors, especially when more than one item is required.

Once all the material has been reduced to size (as per the cutting list) and checked to see that its face side is not twisted and that all the face edges are square with their respective face sides, the marking-out process can begin.

Figure 2.8 illustrates a typical marking-out procedure for a simple mortise-and-tenoned frame.

Marking-out tools

Try-squares (fig. 2.9)   As their name suggests, these test pieces of timber for squareness or are used for marking lines at right angles from either a face side or a face edge.

It is advisable periodically to test the try-square for squareness (see fig. 2.9(a)). Misalignment could be due to misuse or accidentally dropping it on to the floor.

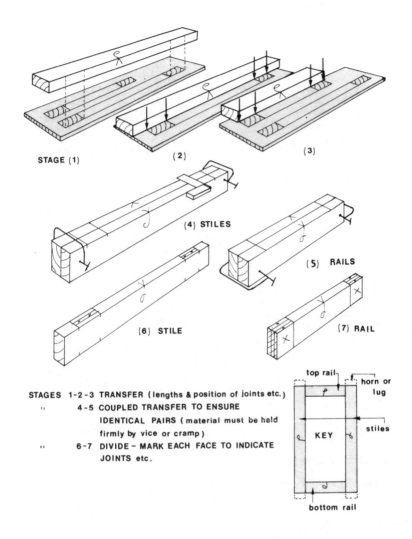

STAGE (1) (2) (3)

(4) STILES

(5) RAILS

(6) STILE

(7) RAIL

STAGES 1-2-3 TRANSFER (lengths & position of joints etc.)

" 4-5 COUPLED TRANSFER TO ENSURE
IDENTICAL PAIRS (material must be held
firmly by vice or cramp)

" 6-7 DIVIDE – MARK EACH FACE TO INDICATE
JOINTS etc.

top rail · horn or lug

KEY · stiles

bottom rail

Fig. 2.8 Typical marking-out procedure for a mortise-and-tenoned frame

Combination square (fig. 2.9(b)) This can be used as a try square, but has the added advantage of being very versatile, in that it has many other uses, e.g. as a mitre square (marking and testing angles of 45°), height gauge, depth gauge, marking gauge (see fig. 2.4), spirit-level (some models only), and rule.

It is common practice to use a pencil with a square, as shown in fig. 2.9(c), although a marking knife (fig. 2.9(d)) is sometimes used in its

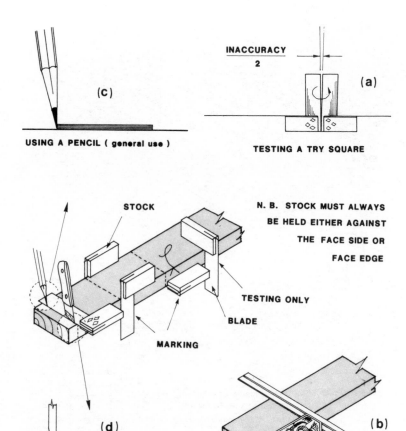

Fig. 2.9 Using try squares

place (especially when working with hardwoods) to cut across the first few layers of fibres so that the saw cut which follows leaves a sharp clean edge, e.g. at the shoulder line of a tenon.

Marking and mortise gauges (fig. 2.10) As can be seen from the diagram, these gauges are similar in appearance and function, i.e. scoring lines parallel to the edge of a piece of timber. The main difference is that the marking gauge scores only a single line but the mortise gauge scores two in one pass. It is possible to buy a gauge that can perform both operations simply by being turned over (see fig. 2.10(b)).

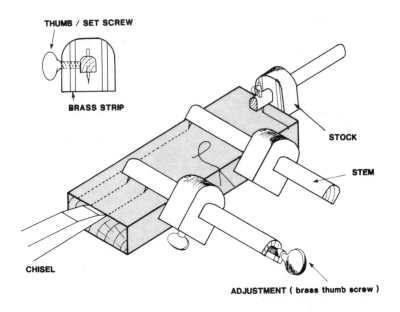

THUMB / SET SCREW

BRASS STRIP

STOCK

STEM

CHISEL

ADJUSTMENT (brass thumb screw)

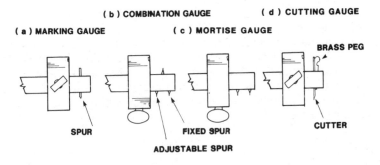

(a) MARKING GAUGE (b) COMBINATION GAUGE (c) MORTISE GAUGE (d) CUTTING GAUGE

BRASS PEG

SPUR FIXED SPUR CUTTER

ADJUSTABLE SPUR

Fig. 2.10 Using marking and mortise gauges

Cutting gauge (fig. 2.10(d))   This is used to cut across the fibres of timber. It therefore has a similar function to that of a marking knife.

Marking angles and bevels
The combination square (previously mentioned, and shown in fig. 2.9) has probably superseded the original mitre square, which looked like a set square but had its blade fixed at 45° and 135° instead of 90°. However two of the most useful pieces of bench equipment when dealing with mitres are a mitre template and a square and mitre template. Examples of their use are shown in fig. 2.11.

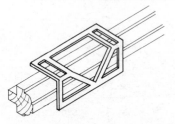

SQUARE OVER MOULDED SECTION

SQUARE & MITRE TEMPLATE

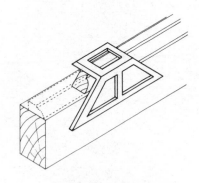

SCORE MITRE PROFILE WITH CHISEL

OR MARKING KNIFE HELD FLAT

MITRE TEMPLATE

N. B. NOT INTENDED AS A CHISEL GUIDE

Fig. 2.11 Marking moulded sections before cutting

Any angles other than 45° will have to be transferred with the aid of either a template pre-marked from the rod or the site situation, or by using a sliding bevel. This has a blade which can slide within the stock and be locked to any angle (fig. 2.12). The bevel as a whole can sometimes prove to be a little cumbersome for marking dovetail joints on narrow boards. This can be overcome quite easily by using a purpose-made dovetail template (see fig. 2.12).

2.3 Saws
Saws are designed to cut both along and across the grain of wood (except the rip saw – see Table 2.1), and the saw's efficiency will be determined by

a) the type and choice of saw,
b) the saw's condition,
c) the application,
d) the material being cut.

Choice of saw
Broadly speaking, saws can be categorised into four groups:

  i) handsaws,
 ii) backed saws,
iii) framed saws,
iv) narrow-blade saws. } for cutting curves

58

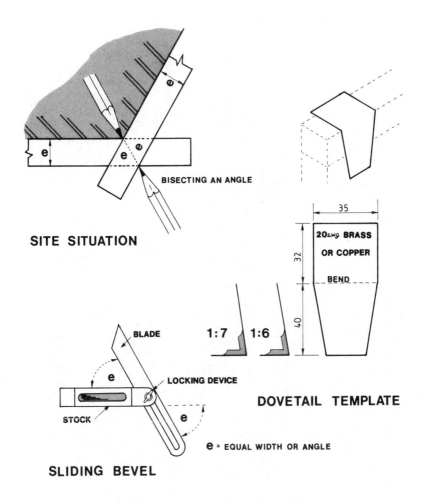

BISECTING AN ANGLE

SITE SITUATION

SLIDING BEVEL

DOVETAIL TEMPLATE

e = EQUAL WIDTH OR ANGLE

Fig. 2.12 Aids for marking and transferring bevels and angles

As can be seen from Table 2.1, each type/group can be further broken down into two or three specifically named saws, which are available in a variety of sizes and shapes to suit particular functions.

Condition of saw
It is important that saws are kept clean (free from rust) and sharp at all times (see section 2.11). Dull or blunt teeth not only reduce the efficiency of the saw, but also render it potentially dangerous. For example, insufficient set could cause the saw to jam in its own kerf and then buckle, or even break (see fig. 2.24).

Table 2.1 Saw factsheet

Type or group	Saw	Function	Blade length (mm)	Teeth shape	Teeth per 25 mm	Handle (insert from fig. 2.13)	Remarks
Handsaws	Rip (fig. 2.14)	Cutting wood with the grain (ripping)	650		4 to 6		Seldom used below 6 teeth per 25 mm
	Cross-cut (fig. 2.15)	Cutting wood across the grain	600 to 650		7 to 8		Can also be used for rip sawing
	Panel (figs 2.16 and 2.17)	Cross-cutting thinner wood and manufactured board (M/B)	500 to 550		10		Easy to use and handle
Backed saws	Tenon (figs 2.18 and 2.19)	Tenons and general bench work	300 to 450		12 to 14		Depth of cut restricted by back strip (blade stiffener)
	Dovetail (fig. 2.20)	Cutting dovetails and fine work	200 to 250		18 to 20		

60

Type or group	Saw	Function	Blade length (mm)	Teeth shape	Teeth per 25 mm	Handle (insert from fig. 2.13)	Remarks
Framed saws	Bow	Cutting curves in heavy sectioned timber and M/B	200 to 300		12 + or −		Radius of cut restricted by blade width
	Coping (fig. 2.21)	Cutting curves in timber and M/B	160		14		Thin narrow blade
	Hacksaw (fig. 2.22)	Cutting hard and soft metals	250 and 300		14 to 32		Small teeth – to cut thin materials. The larger the teeth, the less liable to clog – small frame hacksaw (see fig. 2.23)
Narrow-blade saws	Compass	Cutting slow curves in heavy and large work	300 to 450		10 + or −		Interchangeable blades of various widths – unrestricted by a frame
	Pad or key hole	Enclosed cuts – piercing panels, etc.	200 to 300		10 + or −		Narrow blade partly housed in handle, therefore length adjustable

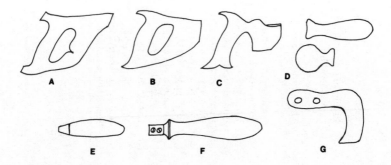

Fig. 2.13 Saw handles

Method of use

The way the saw is used will depend on the following factors:

a) the type and condition of the wood being cut;
b) the direction of cut – ripping or cross-cutting;
c) the location – bench work or site work.

Practical illustrated examples are shown in figs 2.14 to 2.23. Note the emphasis on safety, i.e. the position of hands and blades and body balance etc.

Material being cut

A vast variety of wood species are used in the building industry today, and many, if not all, will at some time be sawn by hand. The modern saw is ideally suited to meet most of the demands made upon it, although there are instances where it will be necessary to modify general sawing techniques, for example when dealing with wood that is

a) very hard,
b) of very high moisture content,
c) extremely resinous,
d) case-hardened.

Occurrence of the above will depend on the type of work being undertaken, and the measures to be adopted will be discussed in volume 2.

Fig. 2.15 Cross-cutting with a handsaw

Fig. 2.14 Ripping with a handsaw

Fig. 2.16 Sawing down the grain (vertically) with a panel saw

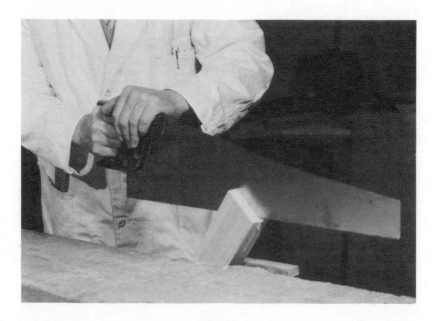

Fig. 2.17 Sawing down the grain — material angled, two saw lines are visible.

Fig. 2.18(a) Tenon saw starting a cut: vice held

Fig. 2.18(b) Tenon saw starting a cut: using a bench hook

65

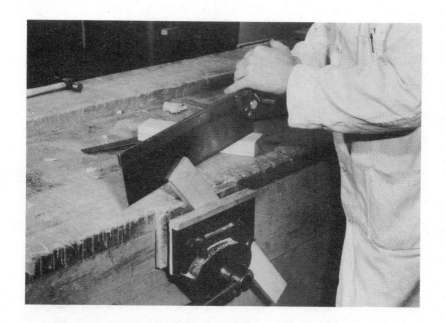

Fig. 2.19 Sawing down the grain − tenon saw

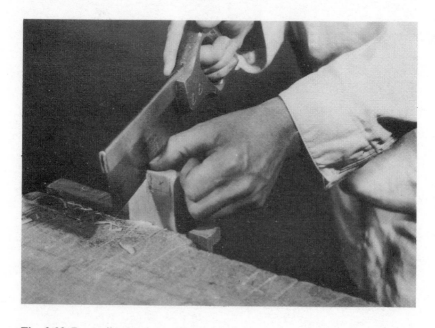

Fig. 2.20 Dovetail saw − starting a cut

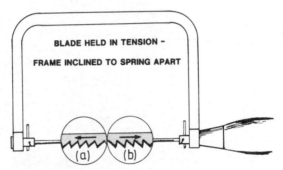

BLADE HELD IN TENSION –

FRAME INCLINED TO SPRING APART

(a) TO CUT ON A FORWARD STROKE, WILL TEND TO BEND OR BREAK THE BLADE.

(b) TO CUT ON A BACK STROKE WILL TEND TO KEEP BLADE TAUT.

Fig. 2.21 Using a coping saw

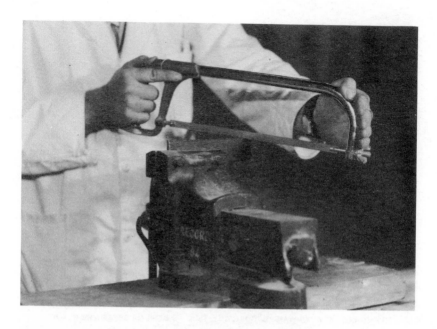

Fig. 2.22 Using a hacksaw

Fig. 2.23 Using a small hacksaw

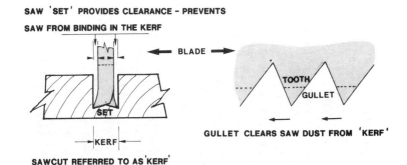

BLADE

TOOTH

GULLET

SET

KERF

GULLET CLEARS SAW DUST FROM 'KERF'

SAWCUT REFERRED TO AS 'KERF'

Fig. 2.24 Providing saw-blade clearance

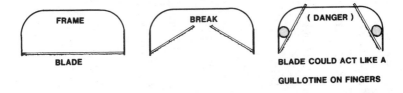

WHEN USING FRAMED SAWS - ESPECIALLY HACKSAWS - ALWAYS KEEP FINGERS

OUTSIDE THEIR FRAMEWORK IN CASE THE BLADE BREAKS.

FRAME

BREAK

(DANGER)

BLADE

BLADE COULD ACT LIKE A

GUILLOTINE ON FINGERS

Fig. 2.25 Frame-saw safety

2.4 Planes

There are many types of plane. All are capable of cutting wood by producing shavings, but not all are designed to produce 'plane' flat surfaces as the name implies. However, as can be seen from Table 2.2, each plane has its own function and, for the sake of convenience, planes have been placed within one of two groups:

 i) bench planes,
ii) special-purpose planes.

Bench planes (figs 2.26 to 2.29)
Wooden-bodied bench planes have been superseded by the all-metal (with the exception of the handle and front knob) plane, although the wooden jack plane is still regarded by some joiners as the ideal site plane, as it is light to handle and less liable to break if dropped. Probably the greatest asset of the wooden bench plane is its ability to remove waste wood rapidly — where accuracy is not too important.

Table 2.2 Plane factsheet

Group	Plane	Function	Length (mm)	Blade width (mm)	Remarks
Bench planes	Smoothing (fig. 2.26)	Finishing flat surfaces	*240, *245, 260	45, 50, 60	50 mm the most common blade width.
	Jack (fig. 2.27)	Processing sawn timber	*355, 380 mm	50, 60	60 mm the most common blade width.
	Fore Jointer (fig. 2.28) (try plane)	Planing long edges (not wider than the plane's sole) straight and true	*455 *560, 610	60 60, 70	The longer the sole, the greater the degree of accuracy.
	Bench rebate (carriage or badger) (fig. 2.29)	Finishing large rebates	235, 330	54	Its blade is exposed on full width of sole.

* Available with corrugated soles (fig. 2.30) which are better when planing resinous timber.

Group	Plane	Function	Length (mm)	Blade width (mm)	Remarks
Special planes	Block (fig. 2.31)	Trimming — end grain	140, 180, 205	42	Cutter seats at 20° or 12° (suitable for trimming laminated plastics), depending on type.
	Circular (compass plane) (fig. 2.32)	Planing convex or concave surfaces	235, 330	54	Spring-steel sole adjusts from flat to either concave or convex.
	Rebate (fig. 2.33)	Cutting rebates with or across the grain	215	38	Both the width and depth of rebate are adjustable.

Group	Plane	Function	Length (mm)	Blade width (mm)	Remarks
	Shoulder/rebate (fig. 2.34)	Fine cuts across grain, and general fine work	152, 204	18, 25, 29, 32	Some makes adapt to chisel planes.
	Bullnose/shoulder/ rebate (fig. 2.35)	As above, plus working into confined corners	100	25, 29	Removable nose – works into corners. Double-bladed – right and left hand. Fitted with depth gauge and/or fence.
	Side rebate (fig. 2.36)	Widening rebates or grooves – with or across grain	140		Both width and depth of groove are adjustable.
	Plough (fig. 2.37)	Cutting grooves of various widths and depths – with and across grain	248	3 to 12	
	Combination	As above – plus rebates, beading, tongues, etc.	254	18 cutters, various shapes and sizes	Not to be confused with a 'multi-plane', which has a range of 24 cutters.
	Open-throat router (fig. 2.38)	Levelling bottoms of grooves, trenches, etc.		6, 12, and V	A fence attachment allows it to follow straight or round edges.
	Spokeshave (fig. 2.39): (a) flat bottom, (b) round bottom (fig. 2.51)	Shaving convex or concave surfaces – depending on type (a) or (b)	250	54	Available with or without 'micro' blade depth adjustment.

Special planes (continued)

71

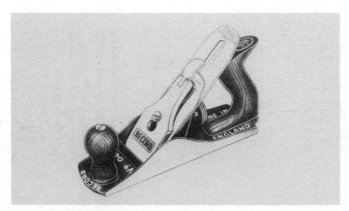

Fig. 2.26 Smoothing plane

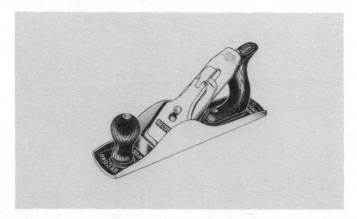

Fig. 2.27 Jack plane

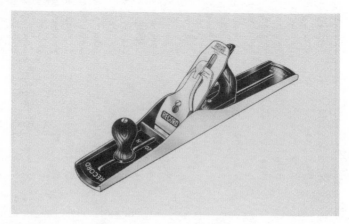

Fig. 2.28 Jointer or try plane

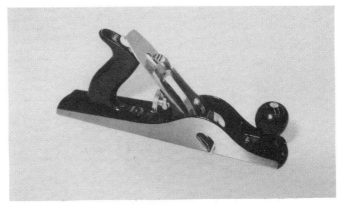

Fig. 2.29 Bench rebate (carriage or badger) plane

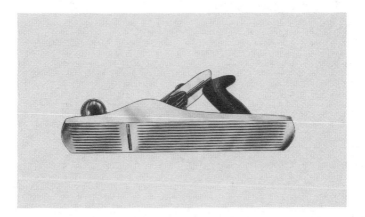

Fig. 2.30 Corrugated sole

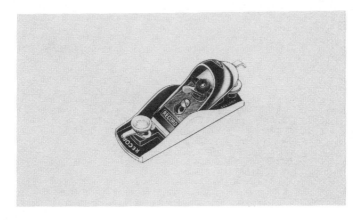

Fig. 2.31 Block plane

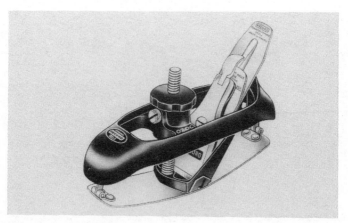

Fig. 2.32 Circular (compass) plane

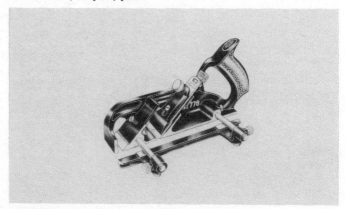

Fig. 2.33 Rebate plane

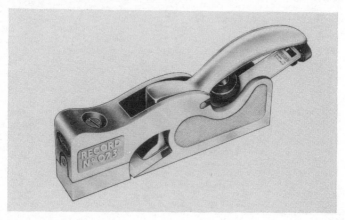

Fig. 2.34 Shoulder/rebate plane

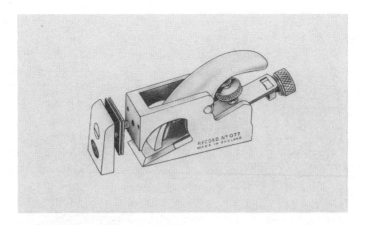

Fig. 2.35 Bullnose/shoulder rebate plane

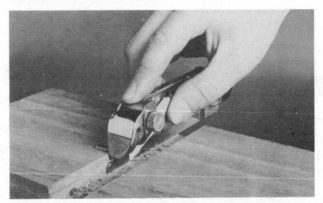

Fig. 2.36 Side rebate plane in use

Fig. 2.37 Plough plane

Fig. 2.38 Open-throat router and its use

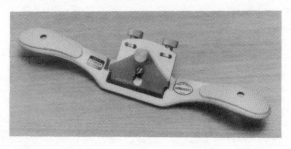

Fig. 2.39 Spoke shave

76

All metal bench planes are similarly constructed with regard to blade angle (45°), adjustment, and alignment (fig. 2.40); variations are primarily due to the size or design of the plane sole, which determines the function (Table 2.2).

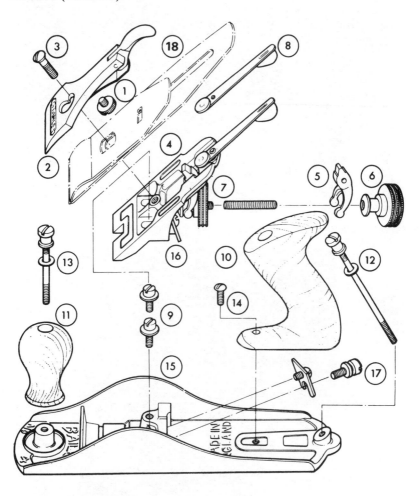

Fig. 2.40 Exploded view of a 'Stanley' bench plane

1 – cap screw
2 – lever cap
3 – lever screw
4 – frog – complete
5 – 'Y' adjusting lever
6 – adjusting nut
7 – adjusting nut screw
8 – L.A. (lateral adjustment) lever
9 – frog screw and washer
10 – plane handle
11 – plane knob
12 – handle screw and nut
13 – knob screw and nut
14 – handle toe screw
15 – plane bottom – sole
16 – frog clip and screw
17 – frog adjusting screw
18 – cutting iron (blade) and cap iron

Fig. 2.41 'Flatting' (planing the surface of) a piece of timber

Fig. 2.42 'Edging' (planing the edge of) a piece of timber

Figures 2.41 and 2.42 show a jack plane being used for flatting and edging a short piece of timber. Notice particularly the position of the hands in relation to the operation being carried out.

Processing a piece of sawn timber by hand is carried out as follows:

i) Select and, using a jack plane, plane a face side (best side) straight (fig. 2.43(a)) and out of twist (fig. 2.43(b)). ('Winding laths' are used to accentuate the degree of twist.) Label the side with a face-side mark (fig. 2.9).

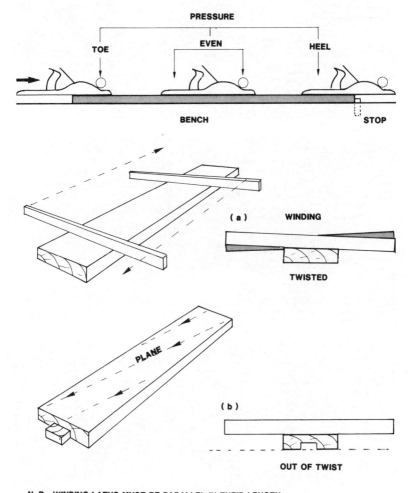

N. B. WINDING LATHS MUST BE PARALLEL IN THEIR LENGTH.

Fig. 2.43 Preparing a face side

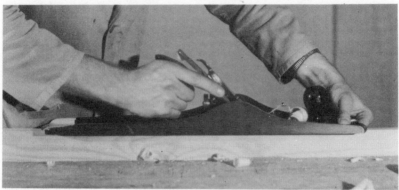

Fig. 2.44 Using a try plane

ii) Plane a face edge straight and square to the face side, using either a jack plane or a try plane (fig. 2.44), depending on the length of the timber being processed. Long lengths will require end support to prevent tipping – this can be achieved by positioning a peg in one of a series of pre-bored holes in the face or leg of the bench, see fig. 2.45. On completion, credit the edge with a face-edge mark (fig. 2.9).

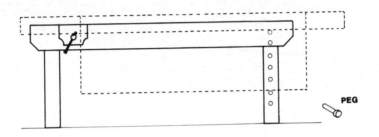

Fig. 2.45 Providing end support

iii) Gauge to width (fig. 2.10), ensuring that the stock of the gauge is held firmly against the face edge at all times, then plane down to the gauge line.
iv) Gauge to thickness – as in step (iii) but this time using the face side as a guide.

Note: when preparing more than one piece of timber for the same job, each operation should be carried out on all pieces before proceeding to the next operation – i.e. face side all pieces, face edge all pieces, and so on.

The smallest and most used of all the bench planes is the smoothing plane. This is very easy to handle and, although designed as a fine finishing plane for dressing joints and surfaces alike, it is used as a general-purpose plane for both bench and site work. Figure 2.46 shows a smoothing plane being used to dress (smooth and flat) a panelled door, and how by tilting the plane it is possible to test for flatness (this applies to all bench planes) – the amount and position of the light showing under its edge will determine whether the surface is round or hollow.

Note: the direction of the plane on the turn at corners or rail junctions – for example, working from stile to rails or rail to stile – will be determined by the direction of the wood grain.

Special planes (figs 2.31 to 2.39)
It should be noted that there are more special planes than the ten planes listed in Table 2.2, and there are also variations in both style and size.

The kinds of planes selected for your tool kit will depend on the type of work you are employed to do. There are, however, about four planes which, if not essential in your work, you should find very useful. They are:

81

Fig. 2.46 Using a smoothing plane to dress a panelled door

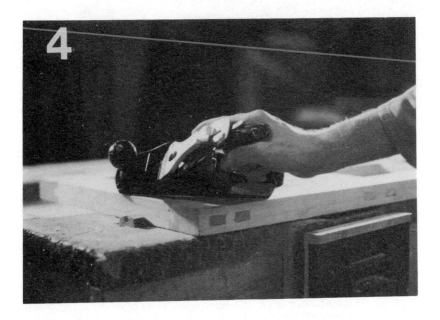

Fig. 2.46 Using a smoothing plane to dress a panelled door *(cont'd)*

a) a block plane (fig. 2.31),
b) a rebate plane (fig. 2.33),
c) a plough plane (fig. 2.37),
d) spokeshaves (fig. 2.39).

Block plane (fig. 2.31)   This is capable of tackling the awkwardest cross grains of both hardwood and softwood, not to mention the edges of manufactured boards and laminated plastics. Some models have the advantage of an adjustable mouth (fig. 2.111) and/or their blade set to an extra low angle of 12°. Such a combination can increase cutting efficiency. Block planes are designed to be used both single- and double-handed.

Rebate plane (fig. 2.33)   Figure 2.47 shows a rebate plane being used to cut a rebate of controlled size, by using a width-guide fence and a depth stop. It is, however, very important that the cutting face of the plane is held firmly and square to the face side or edge of the timber throughout the whole operation.

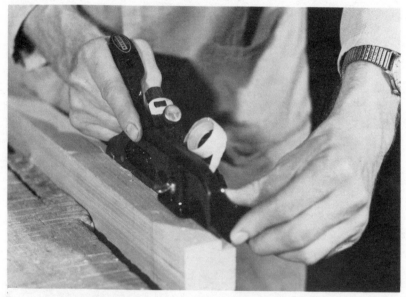

Fig. 2.47 Planing a rebate

Because the blade of a rebate plane has to extend across the whole width of its sole, a cut finger can easily result from careless handling. Particular care should therefore be taken to keep fingers away from the blade during its use, and especially when making the desired depth and/or width adjustments.

84

Plough plane (fig. 2.37) Figure 2.48 shows a plough plane cutting a groove in the edge of a piece of wood. It is also capable of cutting rebates to the cutter widths provided and by the method shown in fig. 2.49.

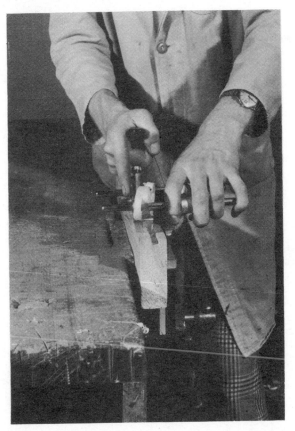

Fig. 2.48 Plough plane cutting a groove

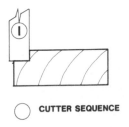

Fig. 2.49 Methods of forming a rebate with a plough plane

The method of applying the plane to the wood is common to both rebate and plough planes, in that the cut should be started at the forward end and be gradually moved back until the process is complete (see fig. 2.50).

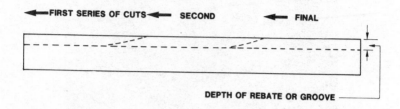

Fig. 2.50 Application of a rebate or plough plane

Spokeshave (fig. 2.39)   This has either a flat or a rounded sole, which determines its use, as can be seen in fig. 2.51.

Fig. 2.51 Spokeshave – use

Joiners often prefer to use larger flat-bottomed planes for shaping convex curves, but the efficiency and ease of operation of a flat-bottomed spokeshave can only be realised when the technique of using this tool has been mastered. Figure 2.52 shows a spokeshave in use – note particularly the position of the thumbs and forefingers, giving good control over the position of the blade in relation to its direction of cut (always with the grain).

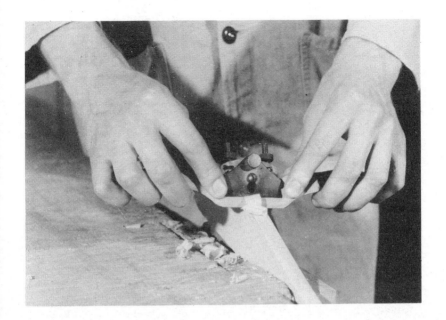

Fig. 2.52 Spokeshave being used

2.5 Boring tools

Boring tools are those tools which are capable of cutting or scraping circular holes of a predetermined size into and below the surface of a given material. They can be divided into three groups:

  i) standard bits,
 ii) special bits,
iii) drills.

   Table 2.3 has classified the above under the headings of:

a) type,
b) function,
c) motive power,
d) hole size,
e) shank section.

(Table 2.3 is meant to be used in conjunction with the illustrations of tools in figs 2.53 to 2.61.)

   The driving force necessary for such tools to operate is provided by hand, by electricity (section 3.1), or by compressed air.

   Hand operations involve the use of a bit- or drill-holder (chuck) operated by a system of levers and gears. There are two main types: the carpenter's brace and the hand drill, also known as the wheel-brace.

Table 2.3 Characteristics of bits and drills in common use. (Not all types are available in metric sizes.)

Group	Type of bit/drill	Function	Motive power	Range of common hole sizes	Shank section	Remarks
Bits (standard)	Centre bit (fig. 2.53)	Cutting shallow holes in wood*	C.B.	$\frac{1}{4}''$ to $2\frac{1}{4}''$	□	
	Irwin-pattern solid-centre auger bit (fig. 2.54)	Boring straight holes in wood*	C.B.	$\frac{1}{4}''$ to $1\frac{1}{2}''$ 6 mm to 38 mm	□	General-purpose bit
	Jennings-pattern auger bit (fig. 2.55)	Boring straight, accurate, smooth holes in wood*	C.B.	$\frac{1}{4}''$ to $1\frac{1}{2}''$	□	
	Jennings-pattern dowel bit (fig. 2.56)	As above, only shorter	C.B.	$\frac{3}{8}''$ and $\frac{1}{2}''$ only	□	Used in conjunction with wood dowel
	Countersink (fig. 2.57)	Enlarging sides of holes to 45°, to receive a screw head	C.B. H.D. E.D.	$\frac{3}{8}''$, $\frac{1}{2}''$, $\frac{5}{8}''$	□ ○	Rose, shell (snail) heads available depending on material being cut and speed

Group	Type of bit/drill	Function	Motive power	Range of common hole sizes	Shank section	Remarks
Bits (special)	Expansive (expansion) bit (fig. 2.58)	Cutting large shallow holes in wood*	C.B.	$\frac{7}{8}''$ to $3''$	□	Adjustable to any diameter within its range
	Forstner bit (fig. 2.59)	Cutting shallow flat-bottomed holes in wood*	C.B. E.D.	$\frac{3}{8}''$ to $2''$	□ ○	Ideal for starting a stopped housing
	Dowel-sharpener bit	Chamfering end of dowel	C.B.		□	Pointed dowel – aids entry into dowel holes
	Turn-screw bit (fig. 2.60)	Driving large screws	C.B.	$\frac{1}{4}''$, $\frac{3}{16}''$, $\frac{3}{8}''$, $\frac{7}{16}''$	□	Very powerful screwdriver
	Flat bit (fig. 2.61)	Bores holes in all forms of wood very quickly and cleanly	E.D.	$\frac{1}{4}''$ to $1\frac{1}{2}''$ 6 mm to 38 mm	⊘	Deep holes may be inclined to wander. Extension shank available.
Drills	Twist drills	Boring wood*, metals, plastics	H.D. E.D. C.A.	$\frac{1}{16}''$ to $\frac{1}{2}''$ 1 mm to 13 mm	○	A few sizes available as □
	Masonry drills (tungsten-carbide tipped)	Boring masonry, brickwork, concrete	H.D. E.D.	No. 6 to no. 20 $\frac{5}{16}''$ to $\frac{3}{8}''$	○	Available for both rotary and percussion-action drills

Key: C.B. – carpenter's brace H.D. – hand drill (wheel-brace) E.D. – electric drill (N.B. Bits used in E.D. must never have a screw point.) C.A. – compressed-air drill □ – square tapered shank ○ – straight rounded shank * – wood and all wood-based products

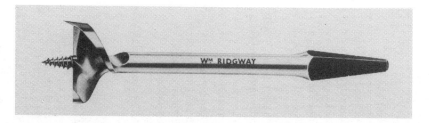

Fig. 2.53 Centre bit

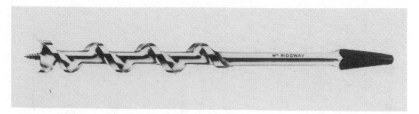

Fig. 2.54 Irwin-pattern solid-centre auger bit

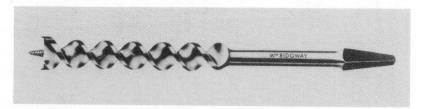

Fig. 2.55 Jennings-pattern auger bit

Fig. 2.56 Jennings-pattern dowel bit

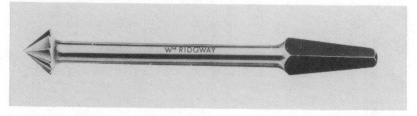

Fig. 2.57 Rosehead countersink

90

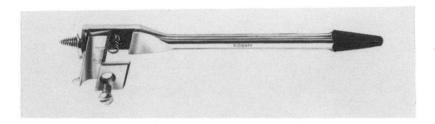

Fig. 2.58 Firmgrip expansive bit

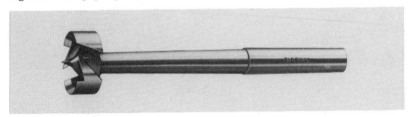

Fig. 2.59 Forstner bit

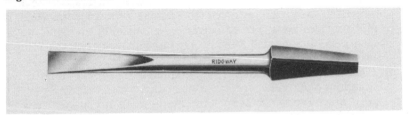

Fig. 2.60 Bright cabinet screwdriver bit (turnscrew)

Fig. 2.61 Flat bit

Carpenter's brace

This has a two-jaw chuck, of either the 'alligator' or the 'universal' type. The alligator type has been designed to take square-tapered shanks, whereas the universal type takes round, tapered, and straight as well as square tapered shanks. The amount of force applied to the bit or drill will depend largely on the 'sweep' of the brace. Figure 2.62 shows how the style and sweep can vary.

91

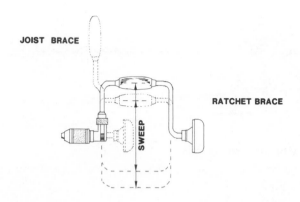

JOIST BRACE

RATCHET BRACE

SWEEP

Fig. 2.62 Types of carpenter's brace

There are three main types of brace:

i) *Ratchet brace* – the ratchet mechanism allows the brace to be used where full sweeps are restricted (an example is shown in fig. 2.63). It also provides extra turning power (by eliminating overhand movement), so often needed when boring large-diameter holes or using a turn-screw bit.

ii) *Plain brace* (non-ratchet type) – limited to use in unrestricted situations only, so not recommended.

iii) *Joist brace* (upright brace) – for use in awkward spaces, between joists for example.

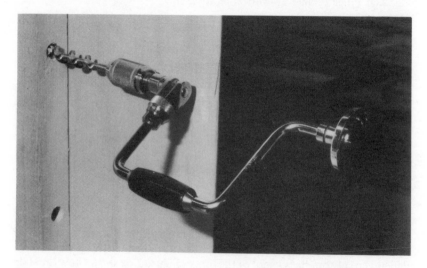

Fig. 2.63 Use of the rachet mechanism

Method of use   Probably the most difficult part of the whole process of boring a hole is keeping the brace either vertical or horizontal to the workpiece throughout the whole operation. Accuracy depends on all-round vision; so, until you have mastered the art of accurately assessing horizontality and verticality, seek assistance.

Figures 2.64 and 2.65 show situations where the assistant directs the operative by simple hand signals. Note also that for vertical boring the operative's head is kept well away from the brace, giving good vision and unrestricted movement to its sweep – only light pressure should be needed if the bit is kept sharp. Horizontal boring support is given to the brace by arm over leg as shown – in this way good balance can be achieved and maintained throughout the process. The stomach should *not* be used as a form of support.

The use of an upturned try-square etc. placed on the bench as a vertical guide is *potentially dangerous* – any sudden downward movement, due to the bit breaking through the workpiece, could result in an accident.

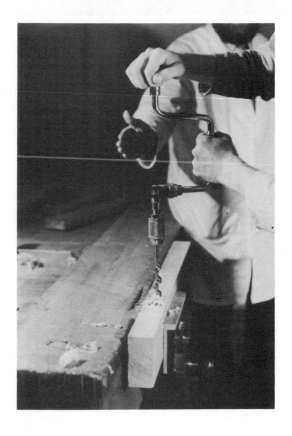

Fig. 2.64 Vertical boring

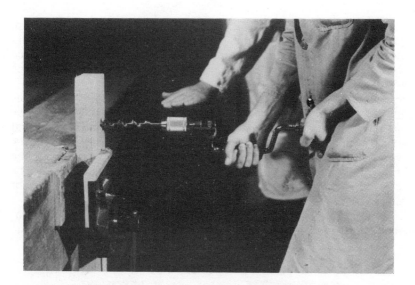

Fig. 2.65 Horizontal boring

Figure 2.66 shows the use and limitations of some of the bits and drills mentioned, together with two methods of breaking through the opposite side of the wood without splitting it, i.e. reversing the direction of the bit or temporarily securing a piece of waste wood to the point of breaking through.

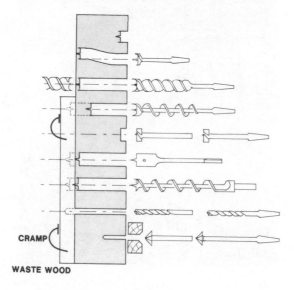

CRAMP

WASTE WOOD

Fig. 2.66 Application of various bits and drills

Fig. 2.67 Hand drill (wheel-brace)

Hand drill (wheel-brace) (fig. 2.67)
This has a three-jaw self-centring chuck, designed specifically to take straight-sided drills. It is used in conjunction with twist drills or masonry drills.

Boring devices and aids
Probably the most common of all boring devices is the bradawl (fig. 2.68) – a steel blade fixed into a wood or plastics handle – used mainly to bore pilot holes for screw threads.

The pump screwdriver, featured under 'driving tools' in section 2.8, may be adapted to drill small short holes and to carry out countersinking operations.

Gauging the depth of a hole can be done either by using a proprietary purpose-made depth gauge or by making your own as in fig. 2.69.

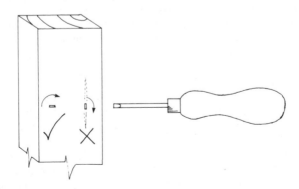

Fig. 2.68 Bradawl (pricker) – application

95

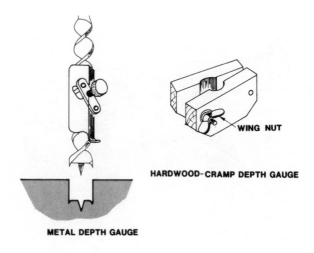

WING NUT

HARDWOOD-CRAMP DEPTH GAUGE

METAL DEPTH GAUGE

Fig. 2.69 Bit-depth gauge

2.6 Chisels

Wood-cutting chisels are designed to meet either general or specific cutting requirements. Table 2.4 lists those chisels in common use, together with their characteristics. Figures 2.70 to 2.75 illustrate some popular examples.

Chisels can be divided into two groups: those which cut by

  i) paring, and
 ii) chopping.

Paring This simply means the act of cutting thin slices of wood − either across end grain (fig. 2.76) or across the grain's length (fig. 2.77). Chisels used for this purpose are slender and designed for easy handling.

Figures 2.76 and 2.77 show two examples of paring. Note especially the method of support given to the body, workpiece, and chisel (both hands behind the cutting edge).

Chopping These chisels are robust, to withstand being struck by a mallet. Their main function is to cut (chop) through end grain − usually to form an opening or mortise hole to receive a tenon; hence the common name 'mortise chisel'.

Figure 2.78 shows a mortise chisel and mallet being used to chop out a mortise hole. Notice the firm support given to the workpiece, and how the G cramp has been laid over on its side so as not to obscure the operative's vision.

96

Table 2.4 Characteristics of woodcutting chisels. (Not all types are available in metric sizes.)

Chisel type	Function	Handle material	Blade widths	Blade section	Remarks
Firmer (fig. 2.70)	Paring and light chopping	H.W. Plastics	$\frac{1}{8}''$ to $1\frac{1}{2}''$ 6 mm to 38 mm		General bench work etc. Plastics-handle types can be lightly struck.
Bevel-edged (fig. 2.71)	As above	H.W. Plastics	$\frac{1}{8}''$ to $1\frac{1}{2}''$ 4 mm to 38 mm		As above – plus ability to cut into acute corners
Paring	Paring long or deep trenches	H.W.	$\frac{1}{4}''$ to $1\frac{1}{2}''$		Extra-long blade
Registered (fig. 2.72)	Chopping and light mortising	H.W.	$\frac{1}{4}''$ to $1\frac{1}{2}''$ 6 mm to 12 mm		Steel ferrule prevents handle splitting.
Mortise (fig. 2.73)	Chopping and heavy mortising	H.W. Plastics	$\frac{1}{4}''$ to $\frac{1}{2}''$		Designed for heavy impact
Gouge – firmer (out-cannel)* (fig. 2.74)	Hollowing into the wood's surface	H.W.	$\frac{1}{4}''$ to $1''$		Size measured across the arc
Gouge – scribing (in-cannel)* (fig. 2.75)	Hollowing an outside surface or edge				Extra-long blades available (paring gouge)

* Out-cannel (firmer) gouges have their cutting bevel ground on the outside; in-cannel (scribing) gouges have it on the inside.

Fig. 2.70 Firmer chisel

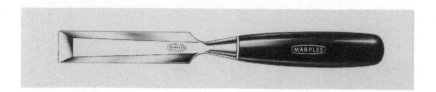

Fig. 2.71 Bevel-edge chisel

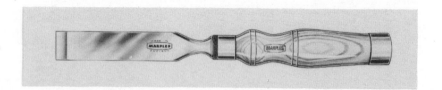

Fig. 2.72 Registered chisel

Fig. 2.73 Mortise chisel

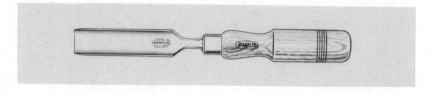

Fig. 2.74 Out-cannel (firmer) gouge

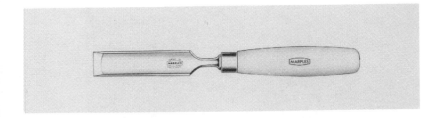

Fig. 2.75 In-cannel (scribing) gouge

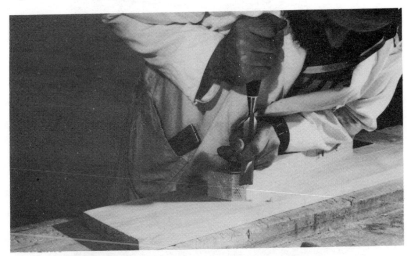

Fig. 2.76 Vertical paring

Fig. 2.77 Horizontal paring

Fig. 2.78 Chopping a mortise hole

2.7 Shaping tools
All cutting tools can be regarded as shaping tools – just as different shapes determine the type or types of tools required to form them. The previous tools should therefore also be included under the heading of 'shaping tools'.

Axe (blocker)
Provided an axe is used correctly, i.e. always keeping fingers and body behind its cutting edge, it is a highly efficient tool – invaluable to the site worker for quick removal of waste wood or for cutting wedges etc. It must be kept sharp, however, and at the finish of each operation the blade must be protected with a thick leather sheath.

Figure 2.79 shows an axe being used to cut a wedged-shaped plug (see chapter 14). Note the piece of waste wood on the floor, to protect both the floor and the axe cutting edge.

Fig. 2.79 Using an axe to cut a wedge-shaped plug

101

Surform tools

These are a very useful versatile range of shaping tools, capable of tackling most materials, depending on the blade (Table 2.5). They are undoubtedly a valuable asset for joiners involved in house maintenance, where conventional tools are often impractical, and the bench-hand will also find these files and shapers very useful.

Figure 2.80 shows just two of these tools, and Table 2.5 shows their blade capabilities.

Table 2.5 Stanley Surform blades

	Standard Cut 21-505 Plane Planerfile Flat File	Fine Cut 21-506 Plane Planerfile Flat File	Half Round 21-507 Plane Planerfile Flat File	Metals & Plastics 21-508 Plane Planerfile Flat File	Round 21-558 Round File	Fine Cut 21-520 Block Plane Ripping Plane	Curved 21-515. Shaver Tool
Hardwoods	■	■	■		■	■	
Softwoods	■	■	■		■	■	
End Grain		■				■	
Chipboard	■		■		■		■
Plywood	■		■		■		■
Blockboard	■		■		■		■
Vinyl	■					■	■
Rubber			■		■		■
Plaster	■		■		■		■
Thermalite	■		■		■		■
Chalk	■		■		■		■
Glass Fibres	■		■		■		■
Brass		■		■	■	■	
Lead		■		■		■	■
Aluminium		■		■	■	■	
Copper		■		■	■	■	
Mild Steel				■	■		
Plastic Laminates		■		■		■	
Plastic Fillers		■	■	■	■		■
Nylon	■			■			■
Linoleum	■			■	■		■
Ceramics		■				■	

102

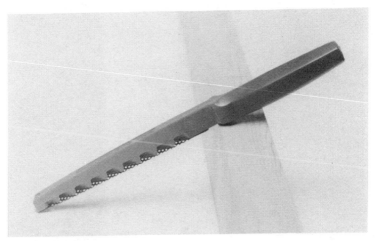

Fig. 2.80 Stanley Surform tools

2.8 Driving tools

These are tools which have been designed to apply a striking or turning force to fixing devices or cutting tools. For example:

a) hammers – striking;
b) mallets – striking;
c) screwdrivers – turning;
d) carpenter's braces – turning; ⎫ dealt with under 'boring
e) hand drills (wheel-braces) – turning. ⎭ tools'

103

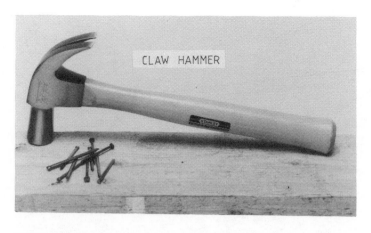

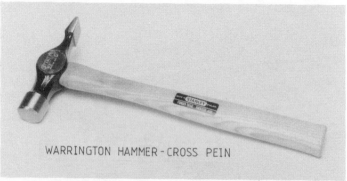

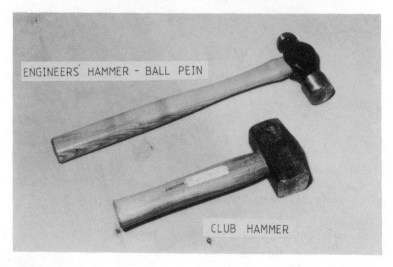

Fig. 2.81 Hammers

104

Hammers

There are four types of hammer you should become familiar with:

  i) claw hammers,
  ii) Warrington or cross-pein hammers,
 iii) engineer's or ball-pein hammers,
 iv) club or lump hammers.

Claw hammers (fig. 2.81)   These are steel-headed with a shaft of wood, steel, or fibreglass and a handgrip of rubber or leather. They are used for driving medium to large nails and are capable of withdrawing them with the claw. Figure 2.82 shows a claw hammer being used to withdraw a nail — notice the waste wood used both to protect the workpiece and to increase leverage.

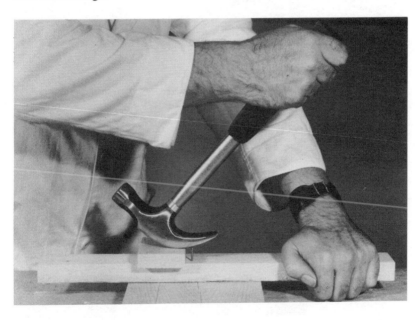

Fig. 2.82 Claw hammer withdrawing a nail

This type of hammer is the obvious choice for site workers involved with medium to heavy constructional work. It can, however, prove cumbersome as the size of nail decreases.

Warrington or cross-pein hammer (fig. 2.81)   Although capable of driving large nails, this is better suited to the middle to lower range, where its cross pein enables nails to be started more easily. This hammer is noted for its ease of handling and good balance.

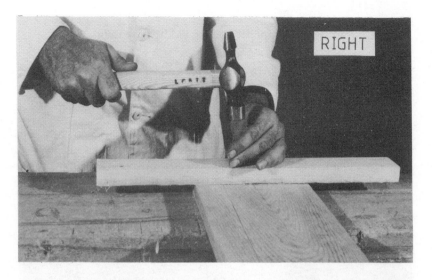

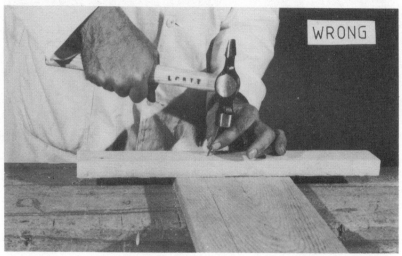

Fig. 2.83 Holding a hammer

Figure 2.83 shows a Warrington hammer being used to demonstrate that, by using the full length of its shaft, less effort is required and greater accuracy is maintained between blows – thus increasing its efficiency. (This applies to all hammers and mallets.)

Tools associated with this hammer are the nail punch (featured in fig. 10.4) and pincers. Pincers provide the means to withdraw the smallest of nails.

Engineer's or ball-pein hammers (fig. 2.81)   The larger sizes are useful as general-purpose heavy hammers and can be used in conjunction with wall-plugging chisels etc.

Club or lump hammer (fig. 2.81)   Used mainly by stone masons and bricklayers, it is, however, a useful addition to your tool kit as a heavy hammer capable of working in awkward and/or confined spaces.

Warning   Hammer heads should never be struck against one another or any hardened metal surface, as this action could result in the head either splitting or splintering – particles could damage your eyes.

If a hammer face becomes greasy or sticky, the chances are that your fingers or workpieces will suffer a glancing blow. Always keep the hammer's striking face clean, by drawing it across a fine abrasive paper several times.

Wooden shafts are still preferred by many craftsmen, probably because of their light weight and good shock-absorbing qualities. Users of wooden-shafted hammers must however make periodic checks to ensure that the head is secure and that there are no hair-line fractures in the shaft. Figure 2.84 illustrates three examples of how a shaft could become damaged.

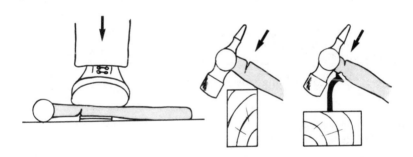

Fig. 2.84 Damage to a wooden shaft

Mallets
The head of a mallet, which provides a large striking face, and its shaft, which is self-tightening (tapered from head to handle), are usually made from beechwood and weigh between 0.4 kg to 0.6 kg – choice will depend on the mallet's use and the user. Many joiners prefer to make their own mallet, in which case it can be made to their own hand.

The joiner's mallet should be used solely to strike the handle of wood-cutting chisels – fig. 2.85 shows its correct use, and fig. 2.78 shows it in use. Using a mallet for knocking together timber frames or joints should

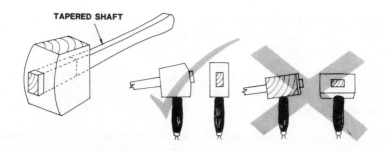

Fig. 2.85 Using a mallet correctly

be regarded as bad practice, because – unless protection is offered to the surface being struck – the mallet will have a similar bruising effect to a hammer.

Screwdrivers
The type and size of screwdriver used should relate not only to the type and size of screw but also to the speed of application and the location and quality of the work.

There are three basic types of screwdriver used by the carpenter and joiner:

  i) the fixed or rigid-blade screwdriver,
 ii) the ratchet screwdriver,
iii) the spiral ratchet or pump screwdriver.

Each is capable of tackling most if not all of the screws described in section 14.2.

Rigid-blade screwdrivers These are available in many different styles and blade lengths, with points to suit any screw head. They work directly on the screw head (screw eye) to give positive driving control. Figure 2.86 illustrates two types of rigid-blade screwdriver.

Ratchet screwdriver This is designed to handle slotted screws and is operated by rotating its firmly gripped handle through 90° – then back – and repeating this action for the duration of the screw's drive. A clockwise or counter-clockwise motion will depend on the ratchet setting – a small sliding button, illustrated in fig. 2.87, is used to pre-select any of the following three operations:

  i) forward position – clockwise motion;
 ii) central position – rigid blade;
iii) backward position – counter-clockwise motion.

Because the driving hand always retains its grip on the screwdriver throughout its operation, this ratchet facility speeds up the process.

108

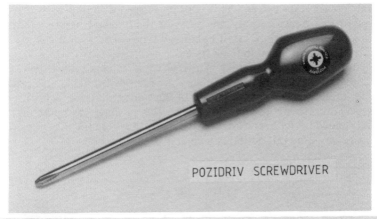

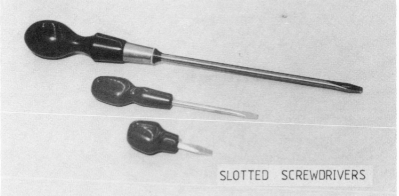

Fig. 2.86 Rigid-blade screwdrivers

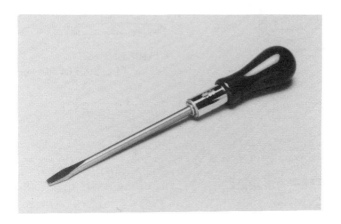

Fig. 2.87 Ratchet screwdriver

109

Spiral ratchet screwdriver This is often termed a 'pump screwdriver', because of its pump action, and is by far the quickest hand method of driving screws. Not only can it handle all types of screws, it can also be adapted to drill and countersink holes.

Figure 2.88 shows a Stanley 'Yankee' spiral ratchet screwdriver, and fig. 2.89 indicates some of the many accessories available. Its ratchet control mechanism is similar to that of the standard ratchet screwdriver; however, its driving action is produced by pushing (compressing) its spring-loaded barrel over a spiral drive shaft, thus rotating the chuck (bit-holder) every time this action is repeated.

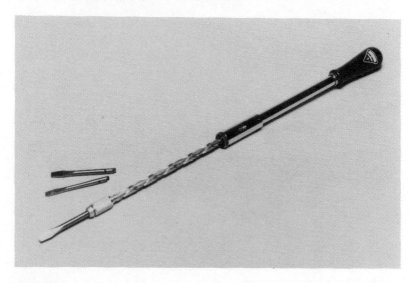

Fig. 2.88 Spiral ratchet screwdriver and bits

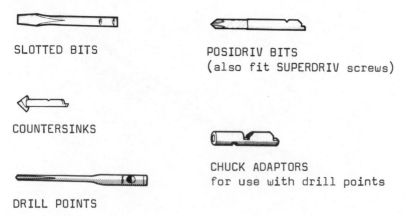

SLOTTED BITS

POSIDRIV BITS
(also fit SUPERDRIV screws)

COUNTERSINKS

CHUCK ADAPTORS
for use with drill points

DRILL POINTS

Fig. 2.89 Some spiral-ratchet-screwdriver accessories

Warning: by turning its knurled locking collar, the spiral drive shaft can be fully retained in the barrel, enabling it to be used as a short rigid or ratchet screwdriver. But, while the shaft is spring-loaded in this position, its point must always be directed away from the operator, as it is possible for the locking device to become disengaged, in which case the shaft will lunge forward at an alarming rate and could result in serious damage or injury.

After use, always *leave this screwdriver with its spiral shaft fully extended. The spring should never be left in compression.*

Screwdriver efficiency   With the exception of the 'stub' (short-blade) screwdriver, the length of blade will correspond to its point size. If driving is to be both effective and efficient, it is therefore important that the point (blade) must fit the screw eye correctly. Figure 2.90 illustrates how face contact with a slotted eye can affect the driving efficiency − (a) and (b) are inclined to come out of the slot; therefore (c) should be maintained at all times.

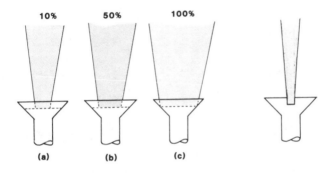

Fig. 2.90 A guide to slot screwdriver efficiency

2.9 Finishing tools and abrasives
The final cleaning-up process will be determined by whether the grain of the wood is to receive a transparent protective coating or is to be obscured by paint. In the former case, treatment will depend on the type and species of wood; whereas the treatment for painting is common to most woods.

Hardwood   Because its main use is decorative, hardwood is usually given a transparent protective coating. Unfortunately, the grain pattern of many hardwoods makes them difficult to work − planing often results in torn or ragged grain. A scraper can resolve this problem, and should be used before finally rubbing down the surface with abrasive paper. Note: always follow the direction of the grain when using abrasive paper before applying a transparent finish (see fig. 2.92).

Softwood Softwood surfaces that require protection are usually painted – there are, however, some exceptions. In preparing a surface for paint, flat surfaces must be flat but not necessarily smooth – unlike with transparent surface treatments, minor grain blemishes etc. will not show. Surface ripples caused by planing machines do show, however, and will require levelling with a smoothing plane, after which an abrasive paper should be used. The small scratch marks left by the abrasive help to form a key between the wood and its priming paint (first sealing coat).

Scraper
This is a piece of hardened steel sheet, the edges of which have been turned to form a 'burr' (cutting edge) – see fig. 2.91(a).

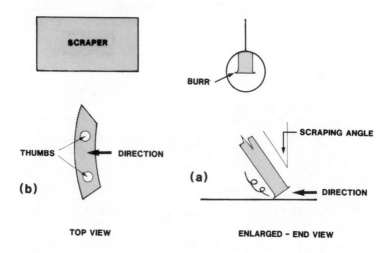

Fig. 2.91 Hand-held scraper

A scraper is either of a type which is held and worked by hand or is set into a scraper plane which looks and is held, like a large spokeshave. Flat scrapers must always be kept bent during use, to avoid digging their sharp corners into the wood (fig. 2.91(b)). Scraper planes, however, can be pre-set to the required cutting angle and simply require pushing.

Sanding
Sanding is the application of abrasive-coated paper or cloth to the surface of wood.

There are several kinds of grit used in the manufacture of abrasive sheets, the two most popular being glass and garnet. Both are available in a sheet size 280 mm × 230 mm and are graded according to their grit size, which ultimately determines the smoothness of the wood – see Table 2.6.

Table 2.6 Comparative grading of abrasive sheets

Abrasive coating	Finish grade									
	Fine			Medium				Coarse		
Glass	00	0	1	$1\frac{1}{2}$	F2		M2		S2	$2\frac{1}{2}$	3
Garnet		5/0	4/0	3/0	2/0	0	$\frac{1}{2}$	1	$1\frac{1}{2}$	

A sanding block should always be used to ensure a uniform surface, be it flat or round. Typical examples are shown in fig. 2.92, together with a method of dividing a sanding sheet into the appropriate number of pieces to suit the blocks.

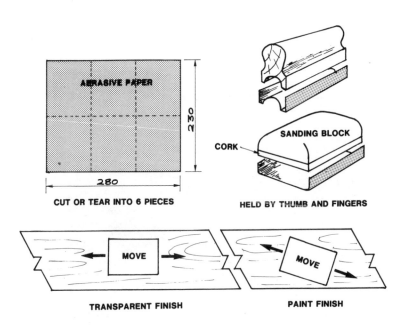

Fig. 2.92 Sanding by hand

2.10 Holding equipment (tools and devices)
Holding tools are general-purpose mechanical aids used in the preparation and assembly of timber components. Holding devices have usually been contrived to meet the needs of a specific job or process, and Table 2.7 gives examples.

113

Table 2.7 Holding equipment

Equipment	Use	
	Preparing material	Assembly aid
Holding tool		
a) Bench vice	Yes	Some models
b) Bench holdfast (fig. 2.93)	Yes	No
c) G cramp (fig. 2.94)	Yes	Yes
d) Sash cramp (fig. 2.95)	Yes	Yes
e) T bar cramp (fig. 2.96)	No	Yes
Holding devices		
f) Bench stop*	Yes	No
g) Bench hook*	Yes	No
h) Mitre block	Yes	No
j) Mitre box	Yes	No
k) Dowel cradle	Yes	No
l) Saw stool (trestle)	Yes	Yes

* Provision can be made in their construction for left- or right-handed users.

Fig. 2.93 Bench holdfast

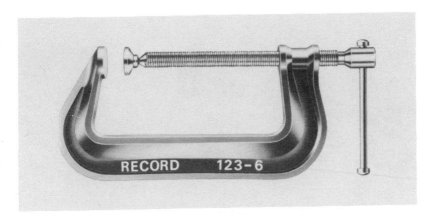

Fig. 2.94(a) G cramp

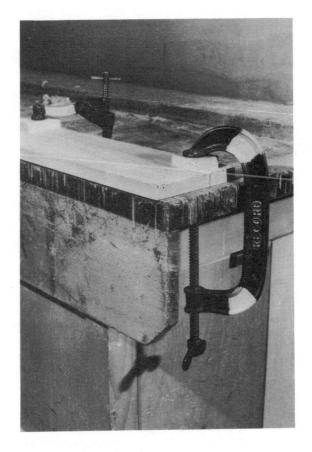

Fig. 2.94(b) G cramp and bench holdfast

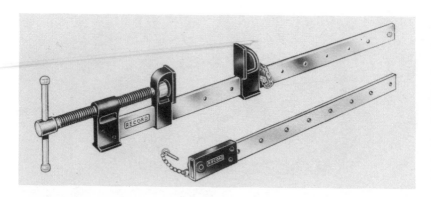

Fig. 2.95 Sash cramp and lengthening bar

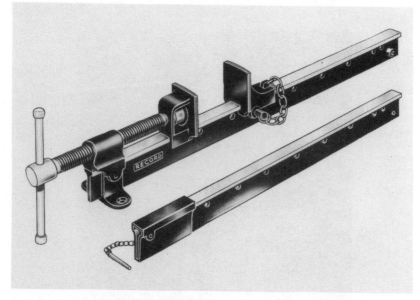

Fig. 2.96 T bar cramp and lengthening bar

Items (a) to (g) in Table 2.7 are mentioned throughout the text and are almost self-explanatory. The mitre block and box, (h) and (j), are devices used to support squared or moulded sections while they are sawn to an angle of 45° degrees. The dowel cradle, (k), holds squared or rounded sections. Saw stools or trestles, (l), are usually used in pairs, either to form a low bench or for support while sawing.

Figure 2.97 features a double-sided work bench, together with items (a), (f), (g), (h), (j), (k), and (l).

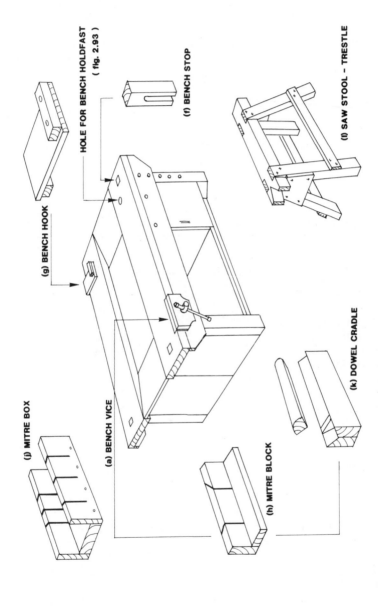

Fig. 2.97 Work bench and holding equipment

HOLE FOR BENCH HOLDFAST (fig. 2.93)

(f) BENCH STOP

(l) SAW STOOL – TRESTLE

(g) BENCH HOOK

(j) MITRE BOX

(a) BENCH VICE

(h) MITRE BLOCK

(k) DOWEL CRADLE

2.11 Tool maintenance

Of all the cutting tools mentioned, only saws and Surforms are purchased ready for use – the remainder will need sharpening.

Once tools have been sharpened, it is only a question of time before they become 'dull' (blunt) again. Some makes of tools dull much quicker than others, due to the quality of steel used to make their blade or cutter, but general dulling is caused either by the type of work or by the abrasive nature of the material being cut. However, other contributory factors include foreign bodies encased in the material being cut, for example hidden nails or screws.

Keeping tools sharp will require varying amounts of skill in the use of those tools and devices associated with tool maintenance. The techniques used for tool maintenance can differ from craftsman to craftsman, and in some cases take many years to perfect. Table 2.8 gives a list of equipment thought necessary for the maintenance of the cutting tools previously discussed.

Table 2.8 Tool-maintenance equipment

Equipment	Tool					
	Drills	Saws	Planes	Bits	Chisels	Screwdrivers
Grindstone (machine)	Yes	–	Yes	–	Yes	Yes
Oilstone	–	–	Yes	–	Yes	Yes
Slipstone	–	Yes	Yes	–	Yes	–
Stropstick	–	–	Yes	–	Yes	–
Oil can	–	–	Yes	–	Yes	–
Mill saw file	–	Yes	–	–	–	–
Saw file	–	Yes	–	Yes	–	–
Needle file	–	–	–	Yes	–	–
Saw vice-clamp	–	Yes	–	–	–	–

Equipment

Grinding machines Every time a blade is sharpened, part of its grinding angle (fig. 2.107) is worn away, making sharpening more difficult. The grinding angle must therefore be re-formed by machine. The grinding machine, together with the relevant regulations, is dealt with in chapter 4.

Oilstones These are used to produce a fine cutting edge (a process called 'honing'). They are generally manufactured from one of three abrasive-grit sizes, producing stones of either fine, medium, or coarse texture. It is possible to purchase a stone with a coarse surface on one side and a fine on the other, called a 'combination stone'.

Oilstones are very brittle and will break or chip unless they are protected. Figure 2.98 illustrates a method of constructing a protective box out of hardwood — half of the oilstone is mortised into the base and half into the lid, and allowance *can* be made for packings at the ends to enable the full length of the stone to be used (see fig. 109). Rubber washers or blocks have been let into or pinned on to the underside, to prevent the box sliding about during use.

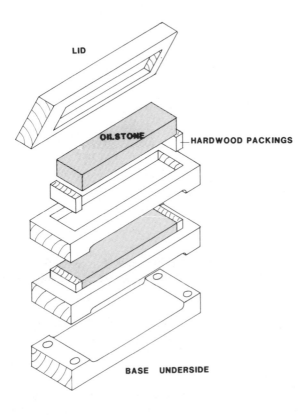

LID

OILSTONE

HARDWOOD PACKINGS

BASE   UNDERSIDE

Fig. 2.98 Oilstone box

Slipstones These are composed in a similar manner to oilstones, but designed to hone the curved cutting edges of gouges and moulding-plane cutters etc. Figure 2.114 shows a slipstone in use — hand held. If a holding device were used, it would leave both hands free to position the gouge or cutter against the stone. Such a device is illustrated in fig. 2.99 and can also serve as a protective box.

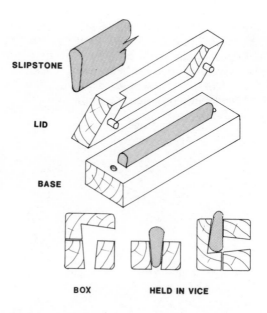

Fig. 2.99 Slipstone box and holding device

Stropstick This gives a blade its final edge. It is made from a thick short length of leather strap, about 50 mm wide, stuck or fixed to a flat board (see fig. 2.109).

Oil Oil provides the stone with the necessary lubrication and prevents the pores of the stone becoming clogged with particles of grit or metal. Only good-quality machine oil should be used; but the very occasional use of paraffin as a substitute often re-establishes the stone's keenness to cut.

Files These are required to sharpen saws and bits. At least two sizes of saw files will be required, together with a flat or mill saw file. Saw files can also be used to sharpen twist bits, but one or two small needle files would prove useful for the smaller sizes of bit. Figure 2.100 shows the different file sections.

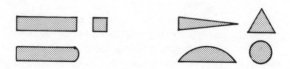

Fig. 2.100 File sections

Holding equipment   There are various aids for holding a tool or cutter while it is being sharpened. When sharpening a saw, it is important that it is held firm and positioned in such a way that the teeth can be seen – preferably without stooping. Figure 2.101 illustrates a device which is ideally suitable for this purpose when either fixed into a bench vice or cramped to a solid object.

Sharpening a spokeshave blade can be difficult and dangerous, due to its shortness. A holder, as shown in fig. 2.102, provides the answer.

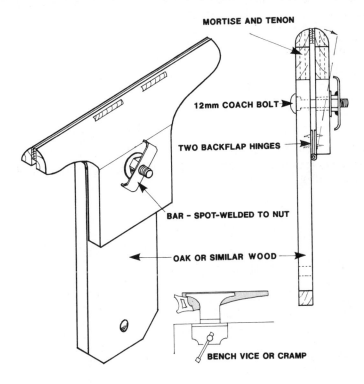

MORTISE AND TENON

12mm COACH BOLT

TWO BACKFLAP HINGES

BAR - SPOT-WELDED TO NUT

OAK OR SIMILAR WOOD

BENCH VICE OR CRAMP

Fig. 2.101 Saw vice

SAW KERF

Fig. 2.102 Spokeshave-blade holder

121

Saws

Of all tools, saws are the most difficult to sharpen. The problem can be lessened, though, if sharpening is carried out at frequent intervals, because as the condition of the saw worsens, so does the task of resharpening. Signs of dullness (bluntness) are the teeth tips becoming shiny, or extra pressure being needed during sawing. The sharpening technique will vary with the type of saw.

If teeth become very distorted, due to inaccurate sharpening or accidentally sawing nails etc., then the following processes should be undertaken:

  i) topping,
 ii) shaping,
iii) setting,
 iv) sharpening.

Topping – bringing all the teeth points in line (fig. 2.103(a)) by lightly drawing a long mill saw file over them. A suitable holding device is shown in fig. 2.103(b).

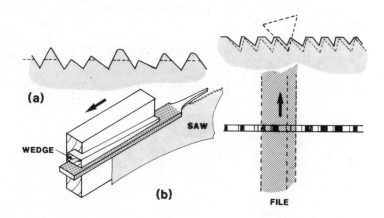

Fig. 2.103 Topping a saw   **Fig. 2.104** Shaping saw teeth

Shaping – restoring the teeth to their original shape and size. The file face should be just more than twice the depth of the teeth and held level and square to the saw blade throughout the process (see fig. 2.104). Shaping is the most difficult process to perfect.

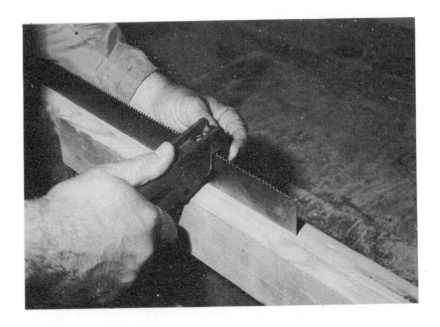

Fig. 2.105 Setting saw teeth

Setting – bending over the tips of the teeth to give the saw blade clearance in its kerf. Manufacturers and 'saw doctors' use a cross-pein hammer and a saw anvil for this purpose. A suitable alternative is to use saw set pliers, which can be operated with one hand simply by pre-selecting the required points per 25 mm of blade, placing over each alternate tooth, and squeezing (fig. 2.105).

Sharpening – putting the cutting edge on the teeth. Cramp the saw, with its handle to your right, as low as practicable in its vice. Place your file against the front face of the first 'toe' tooth set towards you and the back edge of the tooth facing away from you, then angle the file to suit the type of saw or work (fig. 2.106(a)) and, keeping it flat (fig. 2.106(b)) and working from left to right, lightly file each alternate V two or three times (fig. 2.106(c) and (d)). After reaching the handle (heel), turn the saw through 180° and repeat as before, only this time working from right to left (fig. 2.106(c) and (e)).

If the teeth are in a very bad condition, you would be well advised to send your saw to a saw doctor (a specialist in saw maintenance) until you have mastered all the above processes.

Note: whenever a saw is not in use, ensure that its teeth are protected.

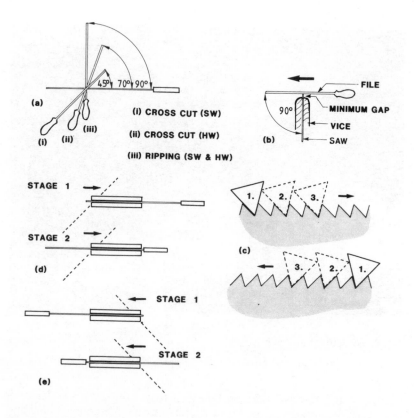

Fig. 2.106 Sharpening saw teeth

Planes

Plane 'irons' (blades) require a grinding angle of 25° and a 'honing' (sharpening) angle of 30° (fig. 2.107) if they are to function efficiently – with one exception: plough planes use a common 35° grinding and honing angle.

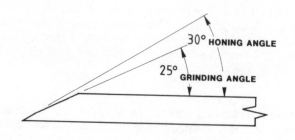

Fig. 2.107 Plane blade – grinding and honing angles

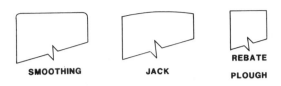

Fig. 2.108 Plane blade shapes

The blade shape should correspond to one of those shown in fig. 2.108. A smoothing-plane blade has its corners rounded to prevent digging in, whereas a jack-plane blade is slightly rounded to encourage quick easy removal of wood. A rebate-plane blade must be square to the iron, for obvious reasons.

Honing   Honing (sharpening) using an oilstone requires much care and attention. The following stages should be carefully studied.

i) Remove the cap iron from the cutting iron – use a large screwdriver to remove the cap screw, *not* the lever cap, otherwise its chrome coating will soon start to peel.

ii) Ensure that the oilstone is firmly held or supported.

iii) Apply a small amount of oil to the surface of the oilstone.

iv) Holding the cutting iron firmly in both hands, position its grinding angle flat on the stone, then lift it slightly – aim at 5° (fig. 2.109(a)).

v) Slowly move the blade forwards and backwards (fig. 2.109(b)) until a small burr has formed at the back. It is important that all the oilstone's surface is covered by this action, to avoid hollowing it (fig. 2.109(c)).

vi) The burr is removed by holding the iron *perfectly flat*, then pushing its blade over the oilstone two or three times (fig. 2.109(d)).

vii) The wire edge left by the burr can be removed by pushing the blade across the corner of a piece of waste wood (fig. 2.109(d)).

viii) If a white line (dullness) is visible on the sharpened edge, repeat stages (v) to (vii). If not, proceed to stage (ix).

ix) Holding the iron as if it were on the oilstone, draw it over the strop stick (fig. 2.109(f)).

The practice of showing off by using the palm of the hand as a strop is dangerous and silly – it can not only result in a cut hand or wrist, but may also cause metal splinters to enter the skin, not to mention the associated problem of oil on the skin.

Blade positions   Bench-plane irons should be positioned as illustrated in fig. 2.110 to ensure effective cutting. The position and angles of cutting irons without cap irons can vary, as can be seen in fig. 2.111, which shows the arrangement for rebate, plough, and block planes.

125

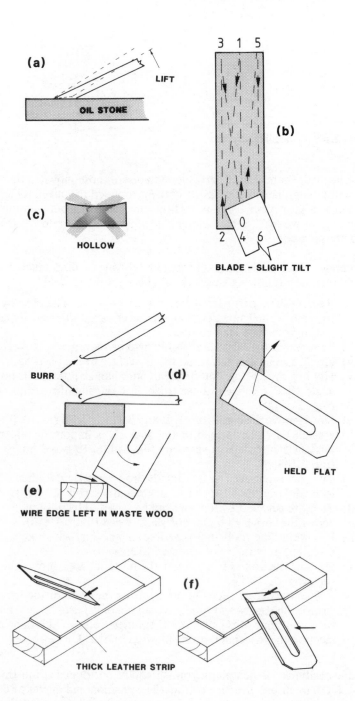

Fig. 2.109 Plane blade sharpening process

126

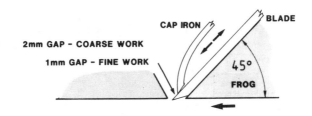

Fig. 2.110 Plane back irons

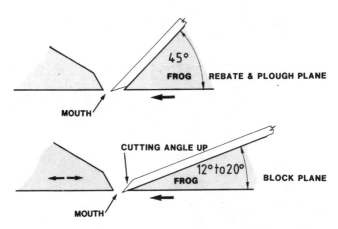

Fig. 2.111 Rebate-, plough-, and block-plane blade arrangement

Chisels

Flat-faced chisels These should be ground and honed to suit the wood they are to cut, as shown in fig. 2.112. However, where access to a grinding machine is difficult, i.e. on site work, it is often possible to extend the useful life of the grinding angle as shown in fig. 2.113.

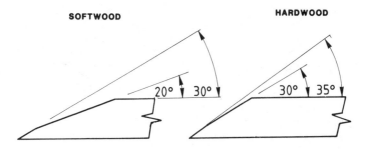

Fig. 2.112 Chisel grinding and honing angles

127

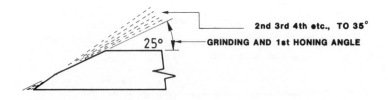

Fig. 2.113 Extending grinding-angle life

The same principles of honing apply as for plane irons, although extra care must be taken not to hollow the oilstone.

Gouges Firmer gouges are ground on a conventional grinding machine – slowly rocking the blade over its abrasive surface. Figure 2.114 shows the method of honing and burr removal. Scribing gouges are ground on a special cone-shaped grinder and honed on a slip stone as shown in fig. 2.115.

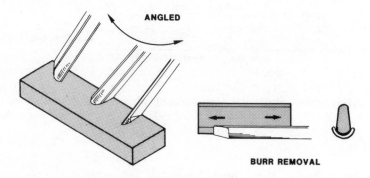

Fig. 2.114 Sharpening an out-cannel firmer gouge

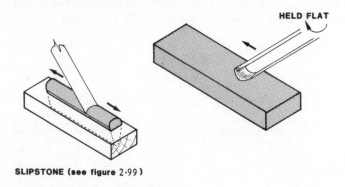

Fig. 2.115 Sharpening an in-cannel scribing gouge

Bits

A twist bit's life is considerably shortened every time it is sharpened, so be sure that sharpening is necessary. The spurs (wings) are usually the first to become dull, followed by the cutters. If the screw point becomes damaged, replace the bit. Figure 2.116 shows the method of sharpening a twist bit.

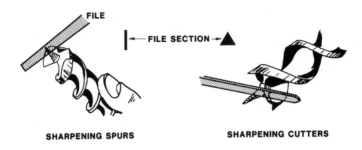

SHARPENING SPURS   **SHARPENING CUTTERS**

Fig. 2.116 Sharpening a twist bit

Screwdrivers

These are the most misused of all hand tools. They have been known to be used as levers, chisels, and scrapers. This is not only bad practice: it is also dangerous. Points do, however, become misshapen after long service, even with correct use. Figure 2.117 illustrates how a point can become misshapen, and possible consequences. The point should be re-formed to suit the screw eye by filing (using a fine-cut file), rubbing over an oilstone, or regrinding (see section 4.9).

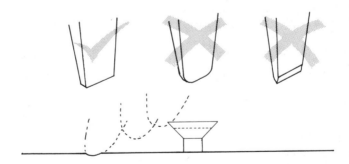

Fig. 2.117 Screwdrivers for slotted screws

3   Portable powered hand tools

Portable electric powered hand tools are available to carry out the following functions:

a) drilling,
b) sawing,
c) planing,
d) rebating,
e) grooving,
f) forming moulds,
g) screw driving,
h) sanding.

Provided a suitable supply of electricity is within easy reach, and the amount of work warrants their use, these tools can be used to speed up hand operations and where the use of permanent machinery would be impracticable.

Some portable power tools are produced specifically for the 'do-it-yourself' market and should not be confused with industrial tools – although they are principally the same, differences occur in both cost and the inability of do-it-yourself tools to sustain constant industrial use. For example:

Type	Category	Use
Light duty	Do-it-yourself	Occasional
Medium duty	General-purpose – tradesman	Moderate to intermittent
Heavy duty	Industrial	Continuous

This volume will deal with the following electrically driven tools:

a) drill,
b) rotary percussion drill (hammer drill),
c) screwdriver,
d) belt sander,
e) orbital sander.

Volume 2 will deal with

a) the circular saw,
b) the reciprocating saw,
c) the planer,
d) the router,
e) the use of cartridge-operated fixing tools.

3.1 Electric drills (fig. 3.1)

Choice of an electric drill will largely depend on

a) the type of work,
b) the volume of work,
c) the size of hole,
d) the type of material.

Figure 3.1(a) shows a 'Wolf Taskmaster' palmgrip drill. Figure 3.1(b) shows the same drill being used to bore a hole in soft masonry (eye protection must be worn during such operations). Figure 3.1(c) illustrates a 'Wolf' back-handle four-speed drill in use.

Ideally, an electric drill should be adjusted to rotate at a speed to suit both the material (workpiece) and the hole size (drill bit). Provided the drill is powerful enough and the correct drill bit (see Table 2.3) is used, it is possible to bore holes in most materials (including soft masonry).

A drill bit should rotate at its most effective cutting speed, otherwise it could overheat, quickly become dull, or even break. Cutting speed is often misquoted as revolutions per minute (rev/min), which only denotes the number of times the chuck revolves every minute (the drill speed). To determine a drill bit's cutting speed (edge speed of bit), the distance it

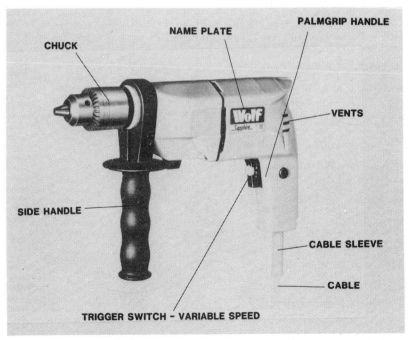

Fig. 3.1(a) Palmgrip electric drill

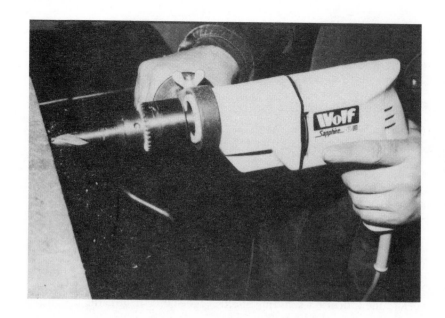

Fig. 3.1(b) Palmgrip electric drill in use

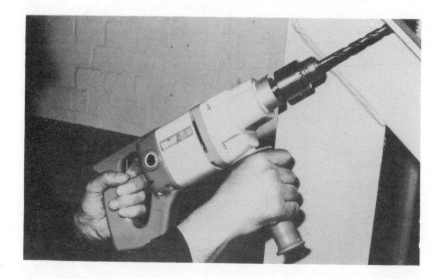

Fig. 3.1(c) Back-handle electric drill in use

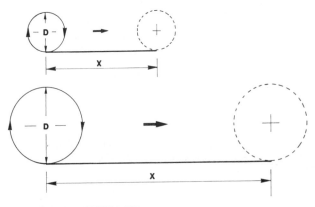

D = DIAMETER OF DRILL BIT

X = DISTANCE COVERED BY CUTTING PERIPHERY (one revolution)

Fig. 3.2 Drill-bit cutting speed

travels every revolution must be known. As can be seen from fig. 3.2, the distance covered by one revolution will vary according to the diameter. Therefore to find the cutting speed of a drill bit − which is usually quoted as metres per second (m/s) − we use the following formula:

cutting speed (m/s) = π × diameter (m) × drill speed (rev/s)

where π('pi') = 22/7 or 3.142

For example, for a drill bit of 6 mm diameter in a drill with a working speed of 1500 rev/min,

cutting speed = π × diameter × drill speed

where   diameter = 6 mm = $\dfrac{6}{1000}$ m

and   drill speed = 1500 rev/min = $\dfrac{1500}{60}$ rev/s

$\therefore$ cutting speed   = $\dfrac{22}{7} \times \dfrac{6}{1000} \times \dfrac{1500}{60}$ m/s

= 0.47 m/s

Drill bits should be used within the recommended ranges of cutting speeds in Table 3.1.

Drilling holes in wood usually requires about twice the cutting speed for metal, but, because of the many hard and abrasive wood-based materials now in common use, consideration should be given to the material's composition before choosing a bit or its speed.

133

Table 3.1 Recommended cutting speeds

Material	Cutting speed (m/s)
Aluminium	1.00 to 1.25
Mild steel	0.40 to 0.50
Cast iron	0.20 to 0.40
Stainless steel	0.15 to 0.20

Drill manufacturers usually recommend the appropriate rev/min to suit both the drill bit size and the material. As a general guide, the larger the hole the lower the rev/min.

Method of use (figs 3.1(b) and (c))
How the drill bit is applied to a workpiece will vary according to the workpiece's size and shape, but it is usually a two-handed operation. It is therefore essential that the work is securely held by a clamp or is such that it will not be affected by the pressure needed to drill the hole. Pressure should be regulated to allow the bit to cut into the material, to keep the hole clear of waste particles, and also to avoid breaking through the under side. Insufficient pressure could result in both the bit and workpiece being overheated, due to heat being generated by friction.

Attachments
Although most manufacturers supply a large range of drill attachments, only those which aid the drilling process should be considered suitable for use by the tradesman; for example,

a) an angle-drilling attachment (fig. 3.3),
b) a drill stand (fig. 3.4),
c) a mortiser (fig. 3.5).

Figure 3.3 shows an angle-drilling attachment in use. This is ideal for getting into awkward corners or spaces between floor joists etc.

A drill stand permits the correct amount of pressure to be applied and leads to greater drilling accuracy. Figure 3.4 shows a bench drill stand being used with a chuck-and-drill-bit guard in position. It is mandatory to fit and use such a guard to comply with the Factories Act 1961 and the Health and Safety at Work Act 1974.

The chisel mortiser works on a similar principle to a drill stand. A special bit drills a hole at the same time as the chisel is paring it square. Figure 3.5(a) labels all the main parts, and fig. 3.5(b) shows it in use − note how the cable from the drill is kept well away from the work bench. This attachment is very effective − mortise holes of up to 13 mm × 13 mm can be cut every time the handle is brought down.

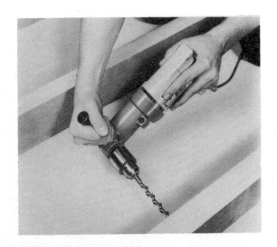

Fig. 3.3 'Wolf' angle-drilling attachment

Fig. 3.4 'Wolf' bench drill stand and drill

135

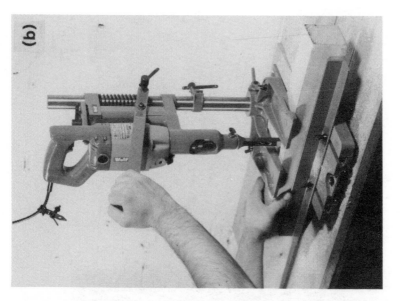

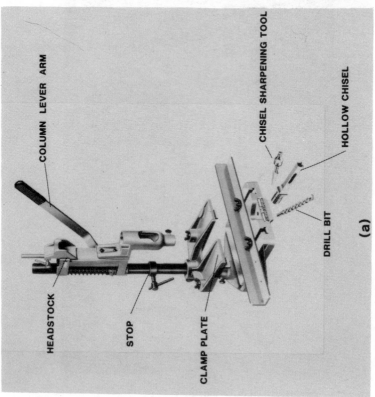

Fig. 3.5 'Wolf' chisel mortiser and stand

136

3.2 Rotary percussion (hammer) drills (fig. 3.6)

These have a dual purpose: they can be used for rotary drilling or, by the turn of a knob or lever, they can be transformed into a percussion drill which with the use of a special tungsten-carbide-tipped drill bit can bore holes into the hardest of masonry or concrete.

Figure 3.6(a) labels the main parts of a 'Wolf Sapphire' rotary percussion drill.

Palmgrip drills can be used for holes up to 10 mm in diameter. Figure 3.6(b) shows a typical example of overhead drilling. Note that the operator is using snug-fitting full goggles, giving complete eye protection, which must be provided and used in such or similar situations to comply with the Protection of Eye Regulations 1974. Notice also the depth-stop attachment.

Back-handled machines allow much larger holes to be bored. Figure 3.6(c) shows such a machine in use. Eye protection in this case is given by using safety glasses.

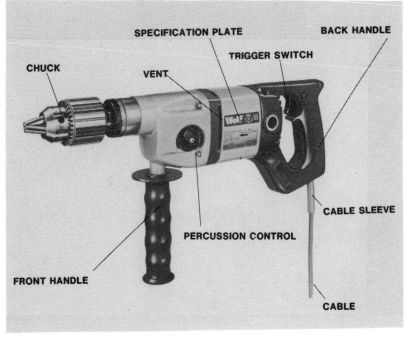

Fig. 3.6(a) Rotary percussion drill

137

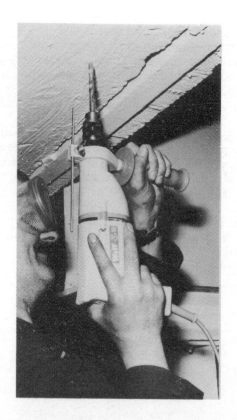

Fig. 3.6(b) Overhead drilling with a palmgrip rotary percussion drill

Fig. 3.6(c) Back-handle rotary percussion drill in use

3.3 Electric screwdriver

This offers a fast virtually effortless method of driving screws. Screwdriver bits of different sizes are available to suit both 'slot' and 'Pozidriv' ('Superdriv') heads.

Method of use

The screwdriver being used in fig. 3.7 is one of a range manufactured by Wolf Electric Tools Ltd, all of which have a mechanism known as a positive clutch with depth-setting device, which enables a screw to be driven to a predetermined depth, after which the screwdriver bit stops turning. The larger screwdrivers are capable of driving woodscrews of up to 100 mm in length. It should be noted that both clearance and pilot holes (fig. 14.4) should be pre-bored before driving any woodscrew.

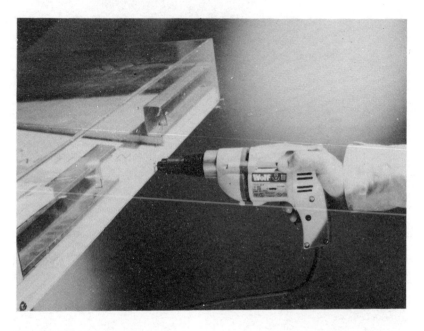

Fig. 3.7 Electric screwdriver

3.4 Belt sander (fig. 3.8)

This is designed and constructed to tackle heavy sanding problems with minimum effort. Figure 3.8(a) names the main parts of this machine. The endless abrasive belt is driven by a motor-driven rear (heel) roller over a front (toe) belt-tensioning roller and then over a steel-faced cork or rubber plate on its base – this is the part that makes contact with the workpiece. Dust is discharged via a suction-induced exhaust into the dust bag.

BACK HANDLE AND TRIGGER SWITCH

SPECIFICATION PLATE

FRONT KNOB

DUST BAG

PRESSURE PAD

ABRASIVE BELT

Fig. 3.8(a) Belt sander

Fig. 3.8(b) Belt sander in use

Method of use

Figure 3.8(b) shows a belt sander being used. It should be permitted to reach full speed before being gently lowered on to the workpiece – allowing its 'heel' to make contact slightly before its 'toe', to avoid any kick-back. When contact is made, there will be a tendency for the sander to move forward and force the workpiece backwards, due to the gripping action of the sanding belt (see fig. 3.9), so both the sander and workpiece must be held firmly at all times. The surface finish produced by the sander will depend on what grade of abrasive belt has been used.

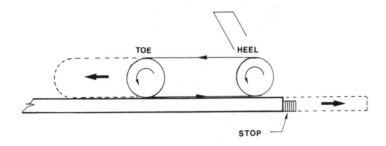

Fig. 3.9 Mechanical action of a belt sander

Note: the dust bag must remain attached to the sander while the motor is in motion, otherwise dust and particles of grit will be discharged directly from the exhaust tube at an alarming rate and could result in serious injury.

3.5 Orbital sander or finishing sander (fig. 3.10)
The main parts of this machine are illustrated in fig. 3.10(a). The abrasive sheet is attached by clips or levers (depending on the design) to a felt or rubber sanding pad which is designed to orbit around a 3 mm diameter at about 12 000 rev/min.

Method of use

Figure 3.10(b) shows an orbital sander being used. The self-weight of the sander is usually sufficient pressure – anything other than light pressure could result in scratching, clogging the paper, or even the body orbiting while the pad remains stationary.

To obtain the best results, the appropriate grade of abrasive paper must be used to suit the job. This often means starting with a coarse grade of paper, then reducing the grade until the desired result is achieved (see section 2.9).

As with all mechanical-sanding operations, dust can be a serious health hazard, and, even though some orbital sanders have dust bags similar to belt sanders, mouth and nose masks will be required during some operations.

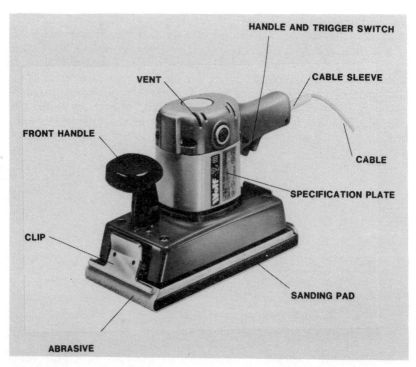

Fig. 3.10(a) Orbital sander

Fig. 3.10(b) Orbital sander in use

142

3.6 Specification plate (S.P.)

A label is fixed to the outer casing of all portable power tools, giving information under some, if not all, of the following headings:

a) *Manufacturer* – maker's name or trade mark.
b) *Type number* – provides a method of identification for attachments or spare parts.
c) *Capacity* – chuck opening size
              – rev/min for 'high' and 'low' speed ratings
d) *Voltage* (potential difference) – the supply must be within the range stated on the S.P.; for example '220/240 V – 105/130 V'. All portable power tools used on building and construction sites should be run from a 110 volt supply, or from higher-voltage supplies which have been suitably reduced via a step-down (centre-tapped) transformer to 110 volts (see fig. 3.13). Reduced voltage greatly reduces the risk of an electric shock being fatal; however, the risk can be further reduced by 'double insulation' (see below).
e) *Wattage* (input on full load) describes the power, or rate of electricity consumption by the motor, expressed in watts, where

$$\text{watts} = \text{volts} \times \text{amperes}$$

f) *Amperage* – the current taken by the motor, expressed in amperes. This can be related to power and voltage:

$$\text{amperes} = \frac{\text{watts}}{\text{volts}}$$

or to voltage and resistance:

$$\text{amperes} = \frac{\text{voltage}}{\text{resistance}}$$

Therefore when the voltage is reduced from 240 V to 110 V the current must be increased if the same power is to be maintained.

g) *Electrical safety* – The Factories Act (Electrical Regulations) 1908 – 1944 protects the user of an electrical appliance by requiring that any metal part of that appliance which could come in contact with a current-conducting wire must be earthed.

Earthing and insulation

Figure 3.11 shows how an electric drill or similar machine is protected by an earth line. The principle is as follows. The neutral of the electrical supply is earthed at the power station or distribution station. If the electrical appliance has a low-resistance connection to earth, then a return path is available for the current if a fault occurs that causes the appliance's casing to become live. This low-resistance path allows a high current to flow which causes the fuse (providing it is correctly rated) to burn out (blow), thus stopping the flow of current and rendering the machine safe.

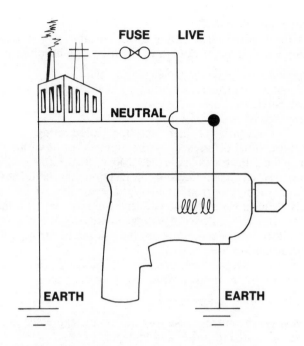

Fig. 3.11 Normal earthed systems

No matter how effective this system might seem, there is always the possibility that it will not work when it is most needed. For example, the system will fail to work if the earth wire has

i) not been connected to the plug socket, or has become defective en route or at source;
ii) become disconnected from the machine;
iii) become disconnected from the plug;
iv) been damaged within the flexible cable to the machine, or the extension lead.

If the earthing system fails to work, possibly for one of the above reasons, it could result in the operator's body being used as an escape route to earth — the results of which could prove fatal.

Fortunately, nearly all portable power tools produced are now *double-insulated*. Figure 3.12 shows how a double barrier is formed around all those components capable of conducting an electrical current. This is achieved by using a strong non-conductive material for the body and/or isolating any metal parts with a non-conductive inner lining, thus eliminating the need for an earth wire. Portable power tools which are double-insulated bear the symbol of a 'square in a square' (fig. 3.12) and, before these tools can legally be used in industry, dispensing with their earth wire,

144

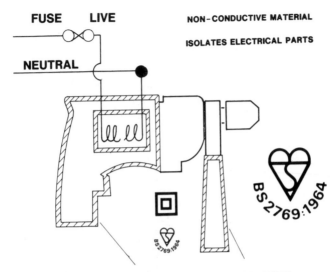

FUSE LIVE NON-CONDUCTIVE MATERIAL

ISOLATES ELECTRICAL PARTS

NEUTRAL

WOLF NON-CONDUCTIVE BODY, SWITCH HANDLE, AND SIDE HANDLE

Fig. 3.12 Double-insulated system

they must comply with the Factories Act (Electrical Regulations) Portable Apparatus Exemption Order 1968 by being approved by the British Standards Institution and bearing BSI's 'Kitemark' BS 2769:1964 on the casing (fig. 3.12).

Double-insulated tools are undoubtedly safer than single-insulated tools (normal earthed systems) but, unless they are powered from a low-voltage supply (110 V), there is still considerable danger from the current-carrying cable.

Figure 3.13 shows how the supply voltage of 240 volts is reduced to 110 volts, with a centrally tapped earth, so that, if a break-down in insulation does occur, the operative should only receive a shock from 55 volts.

3.7 General safety
Before a portable power tool is used, the operator must be confident that all necessary steps have been taken to ensure both his or her safety and that of any persons within close proximity of the operation to be carried out.

The precautions listed below should always be followed:

a) Never use a portable power tool until you have been instructed in its use by a competent person.
b) Only use a portable power tool after authorised approval (the tool in question may have been withdrawn from use for some reason of safety).

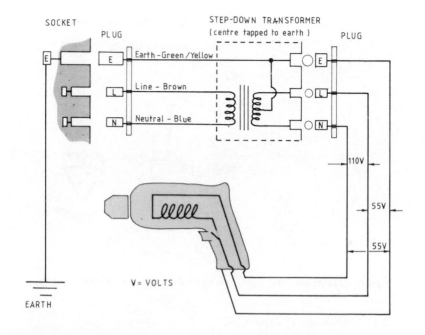

Fig. 3.13 110 volt system

c) The manufacturer's handbook of instruction for the tool in question should be read and understood before use.
d) Always wear sensibly fitting clothes – avoid loose cuffs, ties, and tears etc.
e) Wear eye protection where required by the Protection of Eyes Regulations 1974.
f) Dust masks should be worn where the operative's health may be at risk.
g) Guards, where fitted, must always be used.
h) Never use blunt or damaged cutters.
i) Keep flexible cables away from the workpiece, cutters, and sharp edges and from trailing on the floor.
j) Before changing bits or abrasive sheets or making any adjustments, always disconnect the tool from the electric supply (remove the plug from its socket).
k) If a tool is damaged or found to be defective, return it to the stores or the person responsible for it. Ensure that it is correctly labelled as to the extent of its damage or defect.
l) If injury should occur – no matter how minor – first aid must be applied immediately to avoid the risk of further complications. The incident should then be reported to the person responsible for safety.

146

4 Woodworking machines

The aim of this chapter is to help the student to become aware of the more common types of woodworking machinery that the carpenter and joiner may encounter, to be able to recognise these machines by sight, and to understand the basic function of them. Volume 2 will discuss the use of these machines.

Undoubtedly the most important aspect of any woodworking machine is its safe use. To this effect, set rules and regulations are laid down by law and must be carried out to the letter and enforced at all times. The need for such strict measures will become apparent – especially when one considers that, unlike in most other industries, the majority of our machines are still fed by hand, thus relying on the expertise of the skilled operator, who must concentrate and exercise extreme caution at all times.

4.1 Cross-cutting machines
These machines are designed to cut timber across its grain into predetermined lengths, with a straight, angled, or compound-angular (angled both ways) cut. With a standard blade and/or special cutters, they can also be used to cut a variety of wood joints, for example housing, halving, mitred, dovetailed, and birdsmouth joints.

There are two main types of cross-cut saws: the travelling-head and radial-arm types.

The travelling-head cross-cut saw (pull-over saw)
Figure 4.1 shows a typical saw of this type. The saw, which is driven direct from the motor, is attached to a carriage mounted on a track, which enables the whole unit to be drawn forward (using the pull handle) over the table to make its cut. The return movement is spring-assisted. The length of timber to be cut is supported by a wood or steel roller table and is held against the fence. For cutting repetitive lengths, a graduated rule with adjustable foldaway stops can be provided. Angle and height adjustments are made by operating the various handwheels and levers illustrated.

The radial-arm cross-cut saw (not illustrated)
This carries out similar functions to the travelling-head cross-cut type but differs in its construction by being lighter and having its saw unit, together with its carriage, drawn over the workpiece while they are hung from under an arm which radiates over the table.

Some of these machines are generally more versatile than the travelling-head types, and what helps to make them so is that not only does the

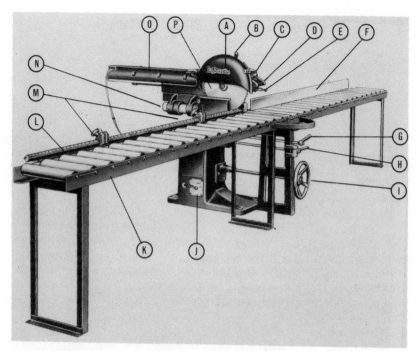

Fig. 4.1 'Robinson' cross-cutting and trenching machine

A – saw guard with adjustable front shield
B – handwheel – tilting saw carriage
C – control – 'start' and 'stop' buttons
D – pull handle
E – brake
F – table fence

G – swivel locking lever
H – swivel adjustment – angle location lever
I – handwheel – to adjust saw vertically (rise and fall)
J – machine isolator

K – roller table
L – cutting-off-gauge bar
M – adjustable stops
N – sawdust exhaust
O – travelling carriage
P – saw blade

carriage arm swivel 45° either way but also the saw carriage tilts from vertical to horizontal and revolves through 360° – enabling ripping, grooving, and moulding operations to be carried out.

4.2 Circular-sawing machines
For the purpose of this chapter, circular-sawing machines will be taken to be those machines which have circular saw blades housed for their greater part inside a metal saw bench and are used to divide squared stock (rectangular- or square-sectioned timber).

Hand-feed circular-saw benches
These are primarily used for resawing timber lengthwise in its width (ripping or flatting) or its depth (deep-cutting or deeping). Some models can

vary the depth at which the blade projects above the saw-bench table.

Figure 4.2 shows a typical general-purpose saw bench with provisions for a cross-cutting fence. The dotted area at the back of the saw bench indicates where a 'backing-off' table must be positioned when anyone is employed to remove cut material from the delivery end (see Regulation 20(2) – volume 2, page 147).

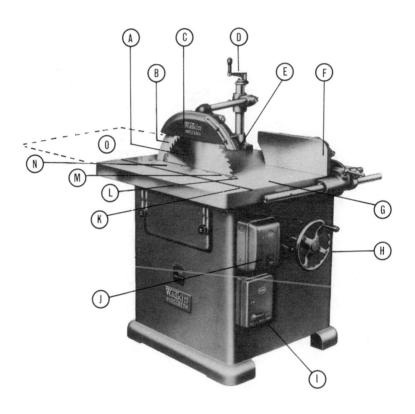

Fig. 4.2 'Wadkin Bursgreen' circular-saw bench

A – saw blade
B – riving knife
C – crown guard
D – crown-guard adjustment
E – extension guard
F – adjustable fence (it will tilt up to 45°)
G – table

H – handwheel – saw-spindle rise and fall
I – isolator
J – control – 'start' and 'stop' buttons
K – machine groove for cross-cutting gauge
L – mouthpiece (hardwood)

M – saw-blade 'packing'
N – finger plate (access to saw spindle)
O – extension table (provision to comply with regulation 20(2))

Saw benches of this type use relatively large saw blades which require 'packings' to help prevent the saw cut deviating from its straight path. Packings are pieces of oil-soaked felt, leather, or similar materials, specially made by the sawyer (wood-cutting machinist) to suit the various types of blade and their relevant position above the saw-bench table. Packings, together with a hardwood 'mouthpiece' and 'backfilling', can be seen in fig. 4.3.

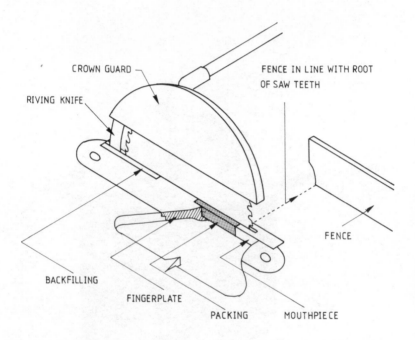

Fig. 4.3 Packing circular saws

The mouthpiece acts as a packing stop and helps prevent the underside of sawn stock from splintering away. Like packings, it will be made to suit each size of saw blade. Backfilling protects the edges of the table from the saw's teeth — one side is fixed to the table; the other to the 'fingerplate'. The fingerplate lifts out the table to facilitate changing a saw blade.

Dimension saw

This uses a smaller saw blade, thus limiting its maximum depth of cut to about 140 mm, depending on the size of blade and the saw-bench capacity. Dimension-saw benches like the one illustrated in fig. 4.4 are capable of carrying out a variety of sawing operations with extreme accuracy and produce a sawn surface which almost gives the appearance of having been planed.

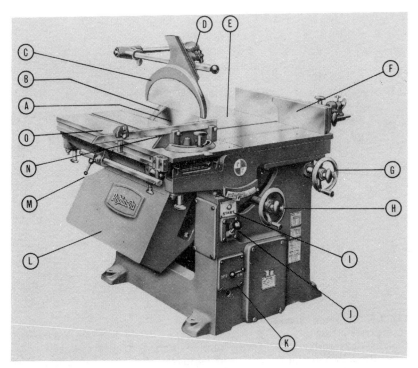

Fig. 4.4 'Robinson' dimension and variety saw

A – saw blade
B – riving knife
C – crown guard
D – crown-guard adjustment
E – main table
F – adjustable fence (it will tilt up to 45°)

G – handwheel – saw rise and fall
H – handwheel – saw tilt adjustment
I – control – 'start' button
J – combined brake and stop lever
K – isolator

L – tilting saw frame
M – sliding-table stop (adjustable)
N – mitre and cross-cut fence and gauge (swivels)
O – sliding table (rolling)

Sawing operations with this saw include ripping, deeping, cross-cutting, mitre and bevelled work, and – provided statutory guarding requirements are met – grooving and moulding. However, for work other than normal sawing operations (usually the most dangerous), effective guarding may not be practicable, in which case that type of work should not be done.

The main features which enable such a variety of operations to be done are

a) adjustable double fence (tilt and length) – adapts to suit both ripping and panel sawing;

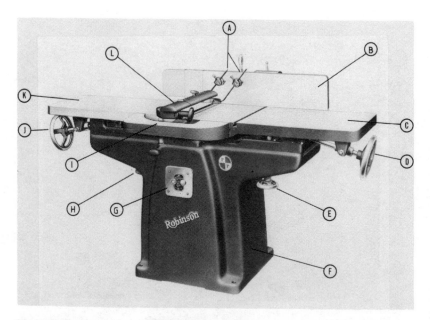

Fig. 4.5 'Robinson' hand-feed planer and surfacer
A – pressure bars (holding-down springs)
B – adjustable fence (it will tilt up to 45°)
C – infeed table
D – handwheel – infeed-table height adjustment
E – handwheel – infeed-table lock

F – main frame
G – control – 'start' and 'stop' buttons
H – handwheel – outfeed-table lock
I – side-support table (extra support while rebating)
J – handwheel – outfeed-table height adjustment

K – outfeed table (delivery table)
L – telescopic bridge guard

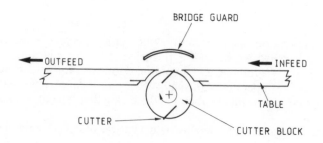

Fig. 4.6 Surfacer cutter-block arrangement

b) cutting-off gauge – allows straight lengths, angles, or single and double mitres to be cut;
c) tilting saw frame and arbor (main spindle) – facilitates bevelled cutting etc.;
d) draw-out table – for access to the saw arbor, for saw or cutter changing;
e) rolling table – for panel cutting and squaring.

4.3 Planing machines

These machines are used to smooth the surface of the wood and reduce sawn timber to a finished size (see fig. 1.19). The first operation – known as 'flatting' – must produce a face side which is straight, flat, and twist-free. This is followed by straightening a face edge which must be square to the face side – known as 'edging'. The timber is then reduced to thickness by planing the opposite faces parallel throughout their length.

Hand-feed planer and surfacer

This is used for planing the face side and face edge. Figure 4.5 illustrates a typical surfacing machine. Its long surfacing table supports the timber as it is passed from the infeed table, over the circular cutter block (see fig. 4.6), to the outfeed table. In accordance with the regulations, cutter guards (bridge and back guards) must always be used during all planing operations. The fence can be moved to any position across the table and be tilted for bevelled work.

Some surfacing machines include in their design facilities to carry out such functions as rebating and moulding. Operations such as these require special means of guarding the cutter and must not be carried out unless such means are provided.

Thicknesser or panel planer

A thicknesser or panel planer such as the one illustrated in fig. 4.7 is used for the final part of the planing process – reducing timber to its finished size.

After the table has been set to the required thickness, timber is placed into the infeed end where it is engaged by a serrated roller which drives it below a cutter block. The machined piece is then delivered from the other end by a smooth roller. Two anti-friction rollers set in the table prevent any drag. The arrangement is shown in fig. 4.8.

Combined hand- and power-feed planer

This is one machine, capable of both surfacing and thicknessing. Figure 4.9 shows such a machine.

Unlike the purpose-made thicknesser, when these machines are used for thicknessing, that part of the cutter block which is exposed on the surfacing table must be effectively guarded throughout its length.

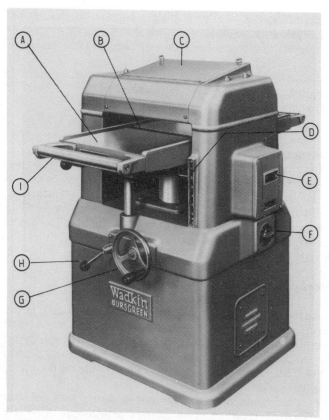

Fig. 4.7 'Wadkin Bursgreen' roller-feed planer and thicknesser

A – thicknessing table (infeed)

B – one of two anti-friction rollers

C – cutter-block guard and chip chute

D – thickness scale

E – control – 'start' and 'stop' buttons

F – feed speed-selector switch (4.5 m/min and 9 m/min)

G – handwheel – raise and lower table

H – lever – table lock

I – outboard roller

4.4 Mortising machines

These machines cut square-sided holes or slots to accommodate a tenon. The hole is made either by a revolving auger bit inside a square tubular chisel or by an endless chain with cutters on the outer edge of each link. Machines are made to accommodate either method or a combination of both.

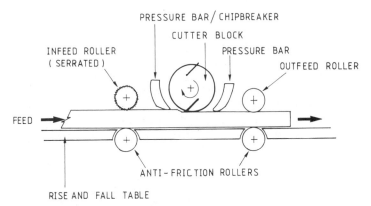

Fig. 4.8 Thicknesser table and cutter-block arrangement

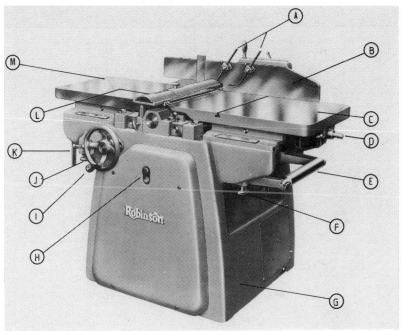

Fig. 4.9 'Robinson' hand- and power-feed planer

A – pressure bars (holding-down springs)
B – adjustable fence (it will tilt up to 45°)
C – infeed table (surfacing)
D – surfacing-table adjustment – raise and lower

E – idle roller to thicknessing table
F – surfacing infeed-table lock
G – main frame
H – control – 'start' and 'stop' buttons
I – handwheel – thicknessing-table rise and fall

J – surfacing outfeed-table (delivery-table) lock
K – finished-thickness scale
L – telescopic bridge guard
M – outfeed table (surfacing)

155

Hollow-chisel mortiser

Figure 4.10 shows the various components of this machine (see also fig. 3.5). As the mortising head is lowered, the auger bores a hole while the chisel pares it square. The chippings are ejected from slots in the chisel side. After reaching the required depth − which for through-mortise holes is about two thirds the depth of the material − the procedure is repeated along the desired length of the mortise. The workpiece is then turned over and reversed end for end, to keep its face side against the fence, and the process is repeated to produce a through mortise (see fig. 4.11).

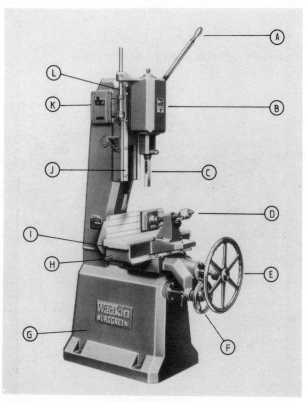

Fig. 4.10 'Wadkin Bursgreen' hollow-chisel mortiser

A − operating levers
B − mortising head (direct motor drive)
C − hollow chisel and auger
D − clamp (faced with a wooden plate)

E − handwheel − operates table longitudinal movement
F − handwheel − operates table cross-traverse
G − main frame
H − table stop bar

I − work table (timber packing) and rear face
J − mortising-head slideway
K − control − 'start' and 'stop' buttons
L − depth-stop bar (mortise depth adjustment)

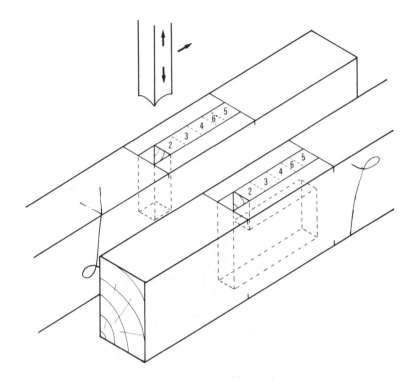

Fig. 4.11 Hollow-chisel mortiser − cutting a mortise hole (viewed from fence side)

Chain and chisel mortiser

Figure 4.12 shows a machine which is capable of mortising by chain as well as by hollow chisel.

The chain mechanism shown in fig. 4.13 consists of the chain, a guide bar and wheel, and a sprocket which turns the chain at high speed.

The guide-bar section (fully guarded at all times) is lowered into the securely held workpiece to cut a large slot (depending on the chain size) in one operation of the lever arm. To prevent the chain splintering away the surface of the wood on its upward motion, a chipbreaker is used.

Using a 'chain' can be much quicker than a 'chisel' but, because of the semicircular-bottomed hole that is left, it is not suitable for short or stub tenons.

The chain mortiser is regarded as being much more dangerous to use than the hollow-chisel machine.

4.5 Narrow band-sawing machines

Unlike those band-saws featured in chapter 1, these machines have blades which do not exceed 50 mm in width. The band-saw illustrated in fig. 4.14 has a maximum blade width of 38 mm.

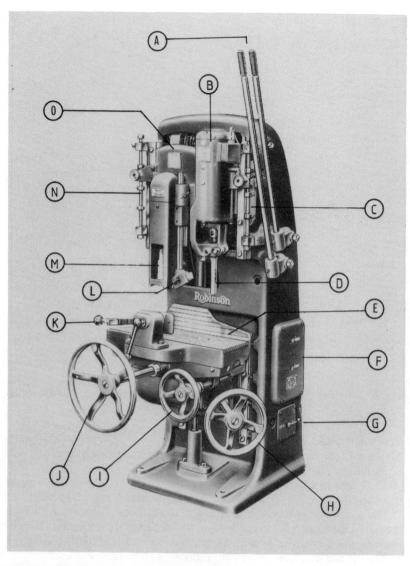

Fig. 4.12 'Robinson' chain and chisel mortiser

A – chain/chisel operating levers
B – chisel headstock
C – chisel mortising, depth-stop arrangement
D – hollow chisel and auger
E – work table (timber packing) and rear face

F – control 'reset' button
G – isolator
H – handwheel – table rise and fall
I – handwheel – operates table cross-traverse
J – handwheel – operates table longitudinal movement

K – clamp
L – chipbreaker
M – chain guard and window
N – chain mortising, depth-stop arrangement
O – chain-mortising headstock

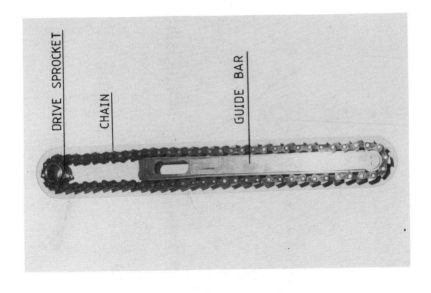

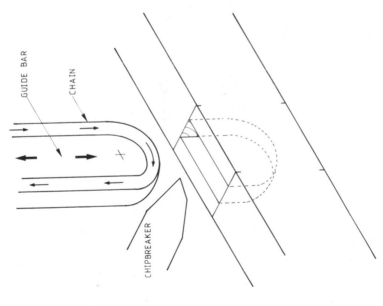

Fig. 4.13 Mortiser-chain mechanism and application

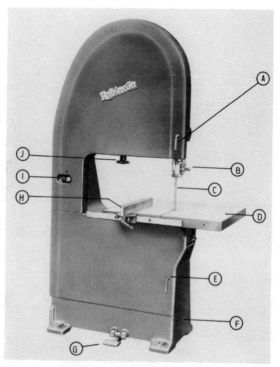

Fig. 4.14 'Robinson' band-saw

A – upper swing-away guard door handle
B – saw guides and thrust wheel (adjustable guard)
C – band-saw blade
D – table (it will tilt up to 45°)
E – lower swing-away guard door handle
F – main frame
G – foot brake
H – fence
I – control – 'start' and 'stop' buttons
J – handwheel – for regulating saw tension

These smaller machines are used for all kinds of sawing, from cutting freehand curves – the radius of which will depend on the blade width (see fig. 4.15) – to ripping, deep-cutting, and cross-cutting. By tilting the table, angled and bevelled cuts can be made.

The machines consist of a main frame on which two large wheels are fixed. The bottom wheel is motor-driven, while the top wheel is driven by the belt action of the saw blade. The wheel rims are covered with a rubber tyre to prevent the blade slipping and to protect its teeth.

To facilitate blade tensioning and alignment, the top wheel can be adjusted vertically and tilted sideways. The amount of tension will depend on the blade width – incorrect tension could result in the blade breaking.

Saw guides give side support to the blade above and below the table while cutting takes place. Back movement of the blade is resisted by a 'thrust wheel' or disc which revolves whenever the blade makes contact. The assembly of guides, thrust wheel, and blade guard adjusts vertically so that it can be positioned as close as practicable to the workpiece (see fig. 4.16).

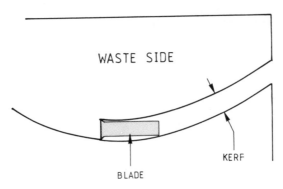

Fig. 4.15 Band-saw – blade and kerf. (Sides of blade must not rub on sides of kerf.)

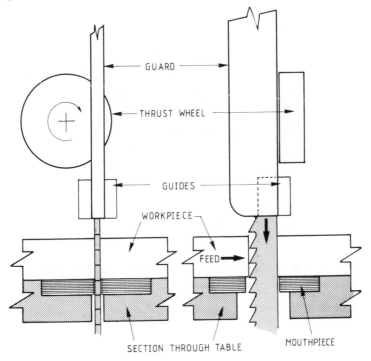

Fig. 4.16 Band-saw – guard, guide, thrust wheel, and table

4.6 Wood-turning lathes

Most students will have seen, if not used, a basic wood-turning lathe during their school days. It was, and still is, a very popular way of introducing students to one of the less dangerous woodworking machines. It is designed to rotate a piece of solid wood while the operator uses a chisel to form it into a round or cylindrical shape.

Wood-turning lathes have changed very little over the years, except that they have become safer to use. There is, however, still a danger of the workpiece working loose and of articles of clothing etc. becoming caught in unguarded moving parts.

Many modern lathes, such as the one shown in fig. 4.17, include in their design such features as simple speed control and a spindle brake. Extra versatility can be given to this machine by attaching a travelling carriage and toolpost to the lathe bed, which allows accurate uniform cuts to be made laterally and transversely in both wood and soft alloy simply by turning the appropriate handwheel.

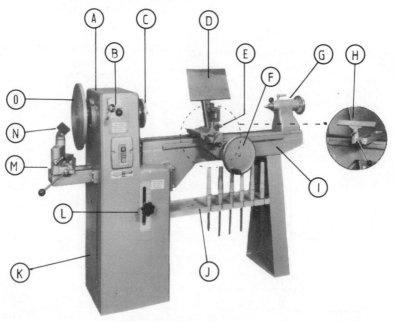

Fig. 4.17 'Dominion' 152 mm centre multi-speed alloy- and wood-turning lathe

A – headstock
B – spindle brake
C – inside face-plate
D – drawing stand
E – compound travelling tool carriage
F – handwheel – carriage movement
G – tailstock
H – standard tool rest, for hand-held chisels
I – lathe bed
J – shelf with turning tools
K – access to headstock column
L – speed control
M – tool-rest support
N – tool rest
O – outside face-plate

162

For forming cylindrical shapes, the workpiece is fixed between two centres — one in the headstock which drives it round, and the other in the tailstock which holds it steady. For bowl or disc shapes, the workpiece is fixed to a face-plate.

Hand wood-turning tools have unmistakable long handles which, when held under the forearm, give good control over their use. These tools fall into two groups. Those which have a true cutting action include gouges, chisels (square and skew), and parting tools. Those having a scraping action — known as 'scrapers' — have a flat face and one under bevel and can be ground to whatever shape is required, whether flat, V, or rounded. Figure 4.18 shows typical blade shapes.

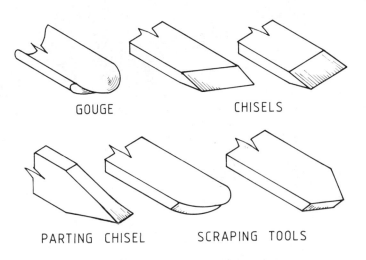

GOUGE   CHISELS

PARTING CHISEL   SCRAPING TOOLS

Fig. 4.18 Wood-turning tools

4.7 Sanding machines

The larger of these machines, like the one illustrated in fig. 4.19, are used mainly to remove marks left by the rotary action of the planers and any ragged grain incurred during the planing process — also to dress (flatten) any uneven joints left after the assembly of such joinery items as doors and windows etc.

Smaller machines, like the combined belt and disc sander in fig. 4.20, can be used with great accuracy for dressing small fitments, truing and trimming end grain, and sanding concave or convex surfaces.

A separate dust-extraction system is essential with all sanding machines.

Wood dust can not only be offensive but can also — depending on the wood species — cause dermatitis and become a contributory factor towards respiratory diseases.

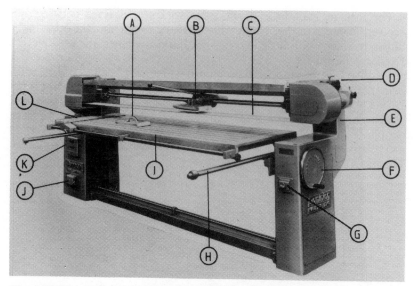

Fig. 4.19 'Dominion' under and over pad belt sanding machine

A – hand pad
B – travelling pressure pad
C – sanding belt
D – belt tracking and tensioning device

E – swan-neck – accommodates long work
F – handwheel – table rise and fall
G – stop button

H – table rails
I – laminated-wood table
J – isolator
K – control – 'start' and 'stop' buttons
L – table fence

4.8 Woodworking Machines Regulations 1974

These regulations impose statutory requirements on the manufacturers, owners, and users of woodworking machinery with regard to the provision and use of guards and safety devices. A suitable working environment must also be provided and maintained.

A brief outline of the areas covered by this sixteen-page document is as follows. Details of working operations are discussed in volume 2.

Part I: application, interpretation, and exemptions

a) Places where these regulations shall apply.
b) Types of machines covered by these regulations – which include portable (hand-held) machines.

Part II: all woodworking machines – general

a) Provision and construction of guards – their adjustment and maintenance.

164

Fig. 4.20 'Wadkin Bursgreen' disc and belt sander

A − sanding disc
(405 mm dia.)
B − sliding adjustable
swivel fence

C − sanding-disc
table − tilts (− 10° to
+ 45°)
D − dust exhaust
E − sanding-belt table
(horizontal or vertical
positions)

F − small-diameter
idler pulley (for sanding
internal curves)
G − sanding belt
H − workpiece stop

b) Siting and position of machine controls.
c) Unobstructed working space.
d) Condition of workshop floors.
e) Temperature of rooms etc. where such machines are used.
f) Training of machine operators − no person will be allowed to operate a woodworking machine unless sufficiently trained to do so, as stated in regulation 13.
g) Duties of persons employed − all safety guards and devices must be used and properly adjusted; any safety defect found − to machines, to their guards or safety devices, or to the surface of the machine-shop floor − must be reported to management.

165

Part III: circular-sawing machines

a) Guarding circular-sawing machines.
b) Size of circular-saw blades.
c) Prohibiting use for cutting rebates, tenons, moulds, or grooves unless the blade is effectively guarded and special precautions are taken.
d) Provision and use of push sticks.
e) Protection of persons employed to remove sawn material from the delivery ends of the machine.

Part IV: multiple rip-sawing machines and straight-line edging machines

Part V: narrow band-sawing machines

a) Provision of guards to saw wheels and blade.

Part VI: planing machines

a) Prohibiting use for cutting rebates, recesses, tenons, or moulds – unless the cutters are effectively guarded.
b) Types of cutter block.
c) Table gap – clearance between cutter and surfacing tables.
d) Provision of bridge guards.
e) Adjustment of bridge guards for flatting and edging operations.
f) Providing cutter-block guards.
g) Providing and using push blocks.
h) Combined machines used for thicknessing.
i) Protection against ejected material.

Part VII: vertical-spindle moulding machines

Part VIII: extraction equipment and maintenance

a) Cleaning saw blades.
b) Provision for the extraction of chips and other particles.
c) Maintenance and fixing of permanent machines.

Part IX: lighting

a) Provision of adequate lighting – natural or artificial without glare.

Part X: noise
Provision of ear protection for persons employed at a machine for periods of eight hours or more at a noise level of 90 dB or more.

4.9 Grinding machines

Some kind of grinding machine is essential in the workshop, to carry out such functions as

a) re-forming the grinding angle on chisel and plane blades (see figs 2.107 and 2.112),
b) regrinding and shaping hand and machine cutters,
c) resharpening screwdriver blades,
d) resharpening cold and plugging chisels.

All the above operations can be done on a dry grinding machine like the one in fig. 4.21. Using this type of grinding machine requires considerable skill in preventing the part of the blade or tool which comes in contact with the high-speed abrasive wheel from becoming overheated (indicated by a blue colour) and loosing its temper (hardness). The end of the blade or tool should be kept cool by periodically dipping it into a dish of water, which should be close at hand.

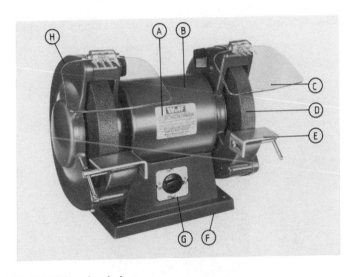

Fig. 4.21 'Wolf' bench grinder
A − specification plate   E − adjustable tool rest   G − machine control
B − motor   F − base plate (fix to   H − grinding-wheel
C − eye shield   bench or stand)   guard
D − grinding wheel

Because of the small diameter of the grinding wheel, chisel and plane blades will have a grinding angle which is hollow (hollow ground), as seen in fig. 4.22. This profile is preferred by many joiners as it tends to last longer than a flat-ground angle.

167

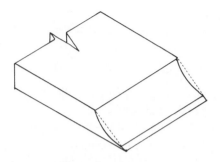

Fig. 4.22 Hollow-ground blades

The problem of overheating can be overcome by using a 'Viceroy' sharp-edge horizontal grinding machine, shown in fig. 4.23. This machine has a built-in coolant system supplied with a special honing oil which flows continually over and through the surface of the grinding wheel while it is in

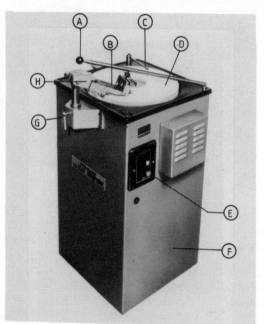

Fig. 4.23 'Viceroy' sharp-edge machine

A – operating lever
B – plane blade holder – reverse side accommodates chisels
C – honing-oil distribution bar

D – grinding wheel
E – control – 'start' and 'stop' buttons
F – cabinet – houses honing-oil container and motor

G – column-height adjusts to suit angle of master arm
H – master arm

168

motion. This machine is primarily used for grinding flat chisel and plane blades; however, there are attachments available which allow gouges and small machine blades to be ground.

The Abrasive Wheels Regulations 1970

These control safety in the use and installation of abrasive wheels, cylinders, discs, or cones. In so doing, they cover the following aspects:

a) maximum permissible speed of wheel to be specified – overspeeding could cause the wheel to burst;
b) proper mounting of the wheels;
c) appointment and training of persons to mount wheels;
d) provision and maintenance of guards and protection flanges;
e) effective means of starting and of cutting off the motive power;
f) workrests to be adjusted as close as practicable to the wheel whenever the machine is in use – otherwise the workpiece could become jammed between the wheel and rest, causing serious injury;
g) condition of the floor around where the machine is to be used.

This short eight-page document should be studied in full, together with the Protection of Eyes Regulations 1974, which stipulate among other things that persons who carry out dry grinding, wheel dressing (an operation which removes metal particles which have become embedded in the wheel), or truing (to keep the wheel concentric with the spindle) must wear approved eye protectors or be protected by a suitable transparent screen or shield against flying particles.

It is, however, advisable to be protected by both a screen and goggles, in case of an unsuspected ricochet.

4.10 Workshop layout

Before any decision is made with regard to workshop layout, some if not all of the following factors should be considered:

a) size of firm;
b) type of work;
c) available space (a clear space of 900 mm plus the maximum length of material to be handled should be allowed around three sides of every machine);
d) work-force – whether full-time wood machinists are to be employed;
e) number and type of machines likely to be cost effective;
f) methods of providing chip- and dust-extraction systems;
g) provision for a tool room (for tool and machine maintenance);
h) storage and racking facilities;
i) suitable and adequate lighting;
j) suitable and sufficient power supply.

Ideally, for a machine shop to work with maximum efficiency, machines should not occupy valuable space unless they are used regularly or contribute towards a steady flow of jobs through the workshop.

Figure 4.24 shows how the machines mentioned in this chapter could be positioned to produce a work flow to suit a small to medium-sized joiners shop. The overall layout does, however, allow for the inclusion of a tenoner and a spindle moulder at a later date. These extra machines (dealt with in volume 2) could be regarded as being essential if the machine shop were to produce joiner items on a production basis.

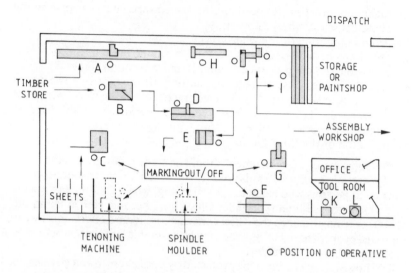

Fig. 4.24 Machine-shop layout

A – cross-cut saw
B – circular-saw bench (rip and general-purpose)
C – dimension-saw bench
D – hand-feed planer and surfacer

E – roller-feed planer and thicknesser
F – mortiser
G – band-saw
H – wood-turning lathe
I – under and over belt sander

J – belt and disc sander
K – 'dry' grinding machine
L – horizontal 'wet' grinding machine

5   Basic woodworking joints

There are many different joints that the carpenter and joiner may use. This chapter is concerned mainly with those made by hand.

Joints generally fall into three categories and carry out the following functions:

Category	Joint	Function
i) Lengthening	End	To increase the effective length of timber
ii) Widening	Edge	To increase the width of wood or manufactured boards
iii) Framing	Angle	To terminate or to change direction

5.1 Lengthening − end joints (fig. 5.1)
Where timber is not long enough, a suitable joint must be made. Figure 5.1(a) shows an end butt joint with cleat. This method would be used only where one face could be concealed.

Figure 5.1(b) shows two methods of making a scarf joint. For structural use they will require a slope of 1 in 12 or less. The second method incorporates a hook which enables the joint to be tightened with folding wedges.

By laminating different lengths of timber together with nails and/or glue, large long lengths of timber can be manufactured. Basic principles are shown in fig. 5.1(c).

A finger joint is shown in fig. 5.1(d). This is produced by machine, then glued and assembled by controlled end pressure. This is a useful method of using up short ends and upgrading timber − after the degraded portion or portions have been removed, the remaining pieces are rejoined.

See also the half-lap joints featured in fig. 5.11.

5.2 Widening − edge joints (fig. 5.2)
Examples of these joints are shown in fig. 5.2. They all enable a board's width to be increased, but whether the joint is to be permanent (glued) or flexible (dry joint) will depend on its location.

Whatever method of joining is chosen, it is always wise to try to visualise how a board will react if subjected to moisture. As stated in chapter 1, tangential-sawn boards are liable to 'cup'. Figure 5.3 shows a way to minimise this effect.

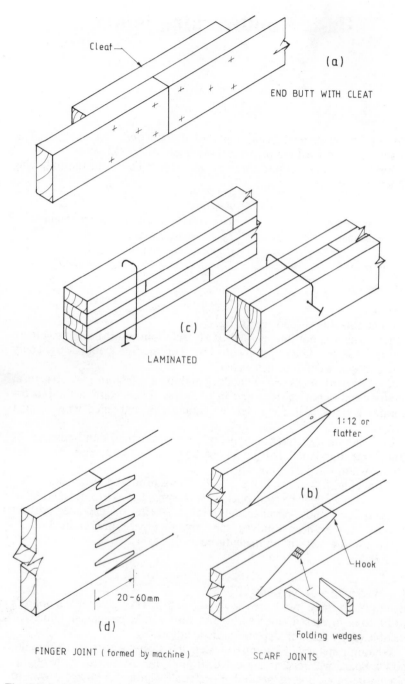

Cleat

(a)

END BUTT WITH CLEAT

(c)

LAMINATED

1:12 or flatter

(b)

Hook

20-60mm

(d)

Folding wedges

FINGER JOINT (formed by machine)

SCARF JOINTS

Fig. 5.1 Lengthening joints. (See also half lap and sloping halving in fig. 5.11.)

172

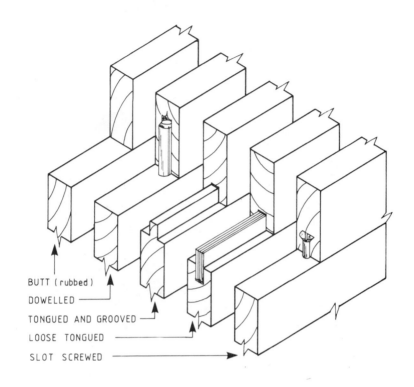

BUTT (rubbed)
DOWELLED
TONGUED AND GROOVED
LOOSE TONGUED
SLOT SCREWED

Fig. 5.2 Widening joints

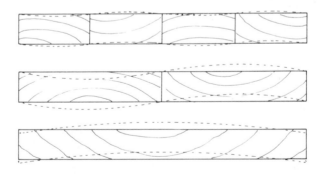

Fig. 5.3 Balancing the effect of moisture movement

Wide solid wood boards cannot generally cope with situations such as floors, walls, ceilings, or doors, etc. as their moisture content is liable to become unstable; therefore a flexible method is used like those shown in fig. 5.4, thus reducing the risk of splitting.

173

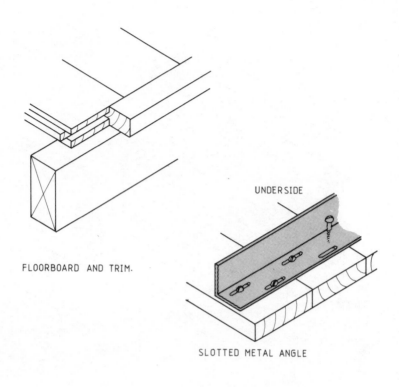

FLOORBOARD AND TRIM.

UNDERSIDE

SLOTTED METAL ANGLE

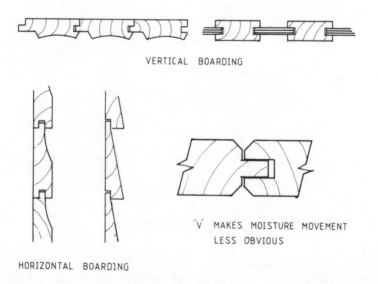

VERTICAL BOARDING

HORIZONTAL BOARDING

'V' MAKES MOISTURE MOVEMENT
LESS OBVIOUS

Fig. 5.4 Joints which are allowed to move

174

Butt joint This is the simplest of all edge joints and is the basis of all the other forms shown in fig. 5.2. If the joint is to be glued, it is important that the adjoining edges match perfectly. Figure 5.5 shows how this is achieved. The boards are first marked in pairs (fig. 5.5(a)), then each pair is planed straight and square by using a long-soled try-plane (fig. 5.5(b)). They are then repositioned edge to edge to check that no light shows through the joint and both faces are in line (fig. 5.5(c)).

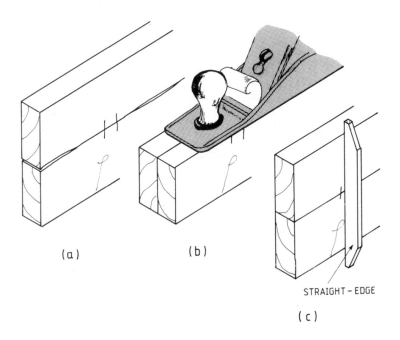

Fig. 5.5 Planing a butt (rubbed) joint

Glue is applied while both edges are positioned as if they were hinged open. They are then turned edge to edge and rubbed one on the other to remove any surplus glue and finally form a bond – hence the term 'rubbed joint'

Dowelled joint By inserting dowels at approximately 300 mm intervals, the butt joint can be both strengthened and stiffened. Figure 5.6 shows how the dowels are positioned and how provision is made for the escape of glue which may become trapped in the hole. (See also fig. 5.17.)

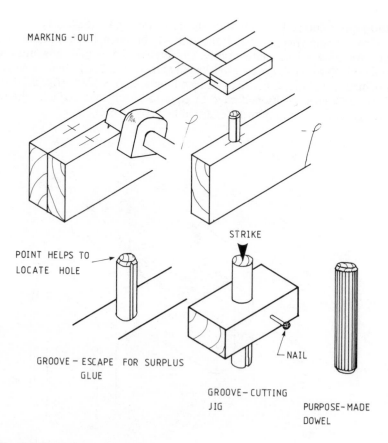

Fig. 5.6 Preparing a dowel joint

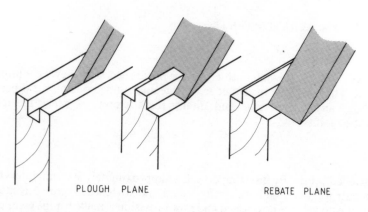

Fig. 5.7 Forming a tongue and groove

176

Tongued-and-grooved joints – loose tongue Another method of strengthening a butt joint is to increase the surface area to be glued (the glue line). These joints do just that. Cutters used to form these joints are shown in fig. 5.7.

Slot-screwed joint This is a simple yet effective method of edge jointing which can also be used whenever a secret fixing is to be made. Figure 5.8 shows how the joint is made. One board is offset by the amount that the screw will travel in the slot (10 to 20 mm, depending on the screw length and gauge) and, when one board is driven over the other, the screw bites into the slot and becomes firmly embedded.

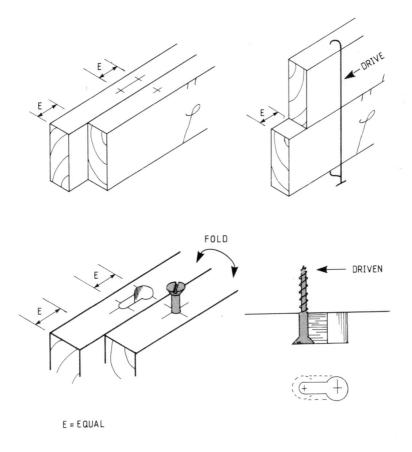

E = EQUAL

Fig. 5.8 Making a slot-screwed edge joint

177

5.3 Framing – angle joints

Joints used to form angles and/or junctions can be divided into the following groups:

a) housing,
b) halving,
c) mortise and tenon,
d) bridle,
e) dowelled,
f) notched and cogged,
g) dovetail,
h) mitre and scribe.

Housing joints The simplest and probably most common housing joint is the 'through' housing (fig. 5.9(a)), which gains bearing support from the notch when formed vertically, and resists side movement when used horizontally as shown. 'Stopped' housings (fig. 5.9(b)) conceal the trench on one edge, and 'double-stopped' housings (fig. 5.9(c)) conceal it on both. 'Dovetailed' housings (fig. 5.9(d)) have one or both (not illustrated) sides of the trench sloping inwards, thereby adding part or total resistance to withdrawal.

With the exception of that in fig. 5.9(d), these joints generally require nailing.

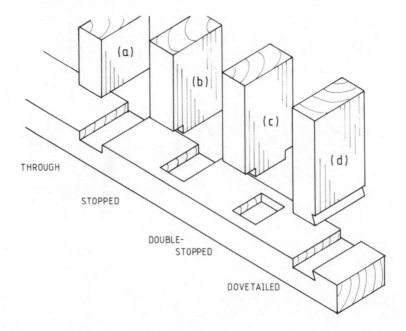

Fig. 5.9 Housing joints (exploded isometric view)

Figure 5.10 illustrates the steps in forming the trench for a stopped housing. They are

a) mark and gauge the width and depth;
b) bore two or more holes to the width and depth of the trench;
c) chop the edges of the holes square;
d) using the 'toe' of a tenon saw, make two or more saw kerfs to the depth line;
e) remove waste wood with a chisel and mallet;
f) level the bottom of the trench with a router.

Housing joints are often used in the construction of shelf and cabinet units, partitions, and sectional timber-framed buildings.

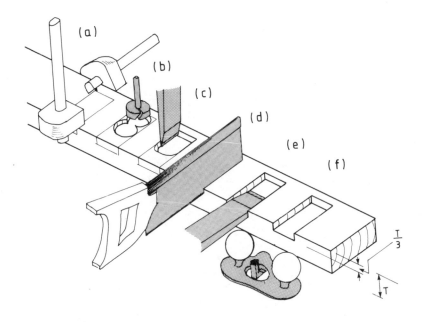

Fig. 5.10 Cutting a housing joint with hand tools

Halving joints These are used where timber members are required either to cross or to lap each other. Named examples, most of which are exploded, are shown in fig. 5.11, where it will be seen that each cut-away portion corresponds with the part it is to join. It is worth noting that the 'half lap' can be used either at a corner – as shown – or as an end joint (end lap) similar to the 'sloping halving' although not as strong.

The joint is made by a combination of those methods used in forming the housing, tenon, and dovetail joints.

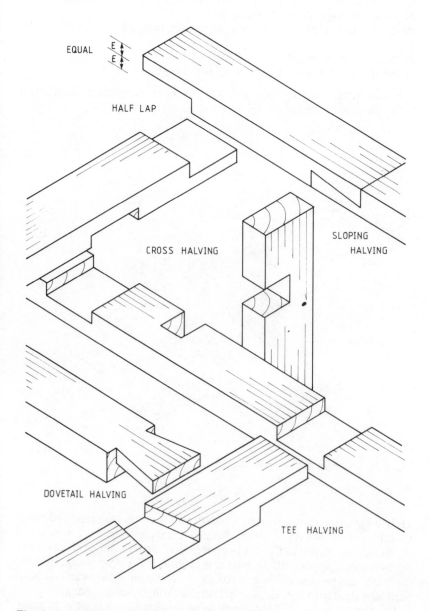

EQUAL

E
E

HALF LAP

CROSS HALVING

SLOPING
HALVING

DOVETAIL HALVING

TEE HALVING

Fig. 5.11 Halving joints (exploded isometric views)

Mortise-and-tenon joints These are the most common of all conventional framing joints – probably due to their versatility and easy concealment. Figure 5.12 illustrates in exploded detail a few examples of how and where these joints are formed and used. The joint's name usually reflects its size, shape, or position; for example

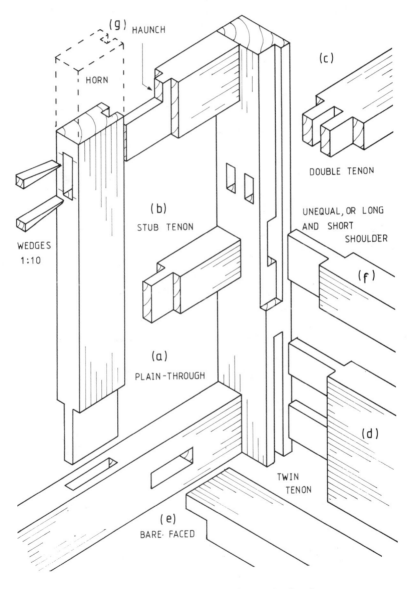

Fig. 5.12 Mortise-and-tenon joints (exploded isometric views)

a) 'through' mortise and tenon – the mortise hole goes completely through the material;
b) 'stub' tenon – mortised only part way into the material;
c) 'double' tenon – two tenons side by side (usually in the thickness of a member);
d) 'twin' tenon – two tenons cut in the depth of a member;
e) 'bare-faced' tenon – only one shoulder;
f) 'unequal shoulder' – one shoulder longer than the other.

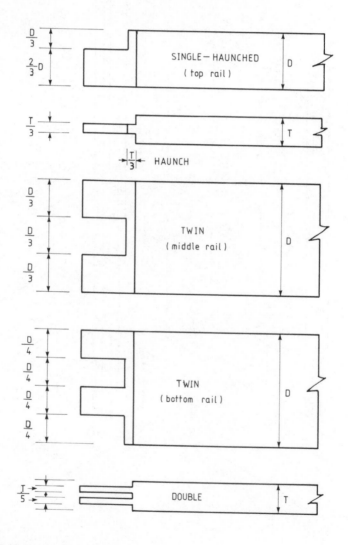

Fig. 5.13 Proportioning a tenon

Haunches (figs 5.12(g) and 5.13)   These serves two purposes: they prevent joints becoming 'bridles' (fig. 5.16) and they reduce the length of the mortise hole which would otherwise be required for wide rails. Figure 5.13 is a general guide as to how tenons and haunches are proportioned.

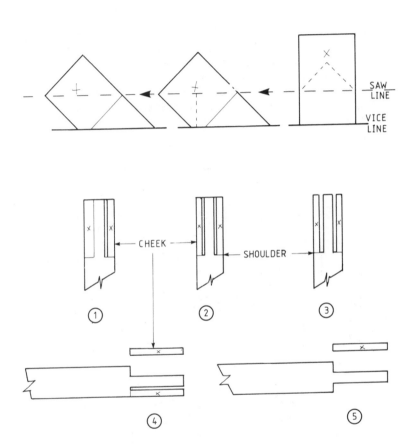

Fig. 5.14 Sequence of cutting a tenon or 'half lap'

Figure 5.14 shows a method of cutting a tenon. The same principles apply to the 'half lap' and 'bridle', although in the latter case, where there are no cheeks, care must be taken to cut on the waste side of the lines. (See also figs 2.17 and 2.19.)

Figure 5.15 illustrates a sequence of operations for chopping out a mortise hole:

a) Set the mortise gauge to the width of the chisel, which should be as near as possible to one third the width of the material being mortised.
b) After having secured the workpiece, chop a hole approximately 15 to 20 mm deep and 4 mm in from one side.
c) Working from left to right or from right to left, chop and gently lever waste wood into the hole formed.
d) Repeat until midway into the workpiece, carefully lifting out chippings at each level. (Note how the waste left on the ends of the hole prevents damage to the mortise hole during this process.)
e) Square the ends of the mortise hole.
f) Turn the workpiece over and repeat the process. (The bench should be protected at this stage if a through mortise is to be cut.) See also fig. 2.78.

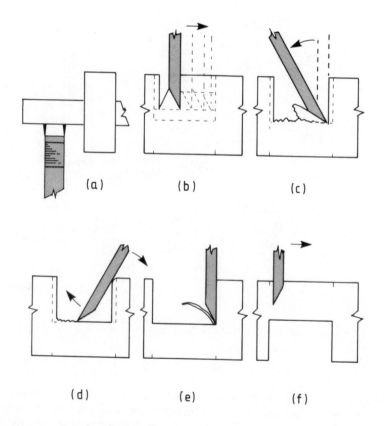

Fig. 5.15 Chopping a mortise hole

Bridle joints Except for the 'corner' bridle — also known as an 'open' or 'slot' mortise — bridle joints slot over through-running members. Named examples are shown in fig. 5.16. They àre cut in a similar manner to tenon and halving joints.

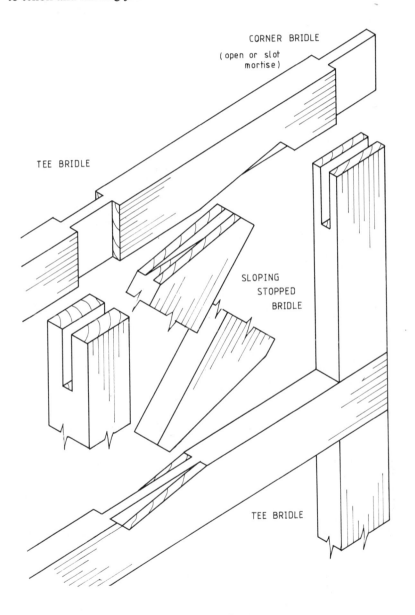

Fig. 5.16 Bridle joints (exploded isometric views)

Dowelled joints These are useful alternatives to mortise-and-tenon joints for joining members in their thickness (fig. 5.17(a)) or as a means of framing members in their width (fig. 5.17(b)). Dowel and hole preparation is similar to the methods shown in fig. 5.6. Correct alignment of dowel with hole is critical, but this problem can be overcome by using a dowelling jig (a template and guide for boring holes accurately).

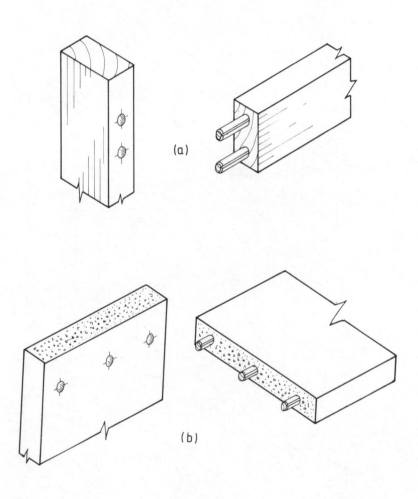

(a)

(b)

Fig. 5.17 Dowelled joints

Notched and cogged joints As shown in fig. 5.18, notches are used to locate members in one or both directions and as a means of making any necessary depth adjustments (joist to wallplates etc.). Cogged joints perform a similar function, but less wood is removed, therefore generally leaving a stronger joint. They do, however, take much longer to make.

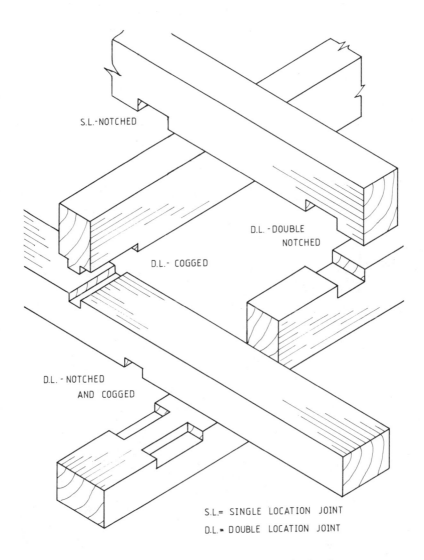

S.L.-NOTCHED

D.L. - DOUBLE NOTCHED

D.L.- COGGED

D.L. - NOTCHED AND COGGED

S.L.= SINGLE LOCATION JOINT
D.L.= DOUBLE LOCATION JOINT

Fig. 5.18 Notched and cogged joints (exploded isometric views)

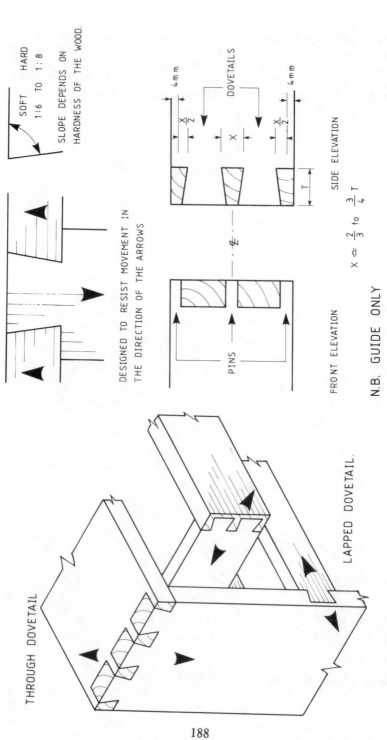

SOFT   HARD
1:6 TO 1:8

SLOPE DEPENDS ON
HARDNESS OF THE WOOD.

DESIGNED TO RESIST MOVEMENT IN
THE DIRECTION OF THE ARROWS

4 mm

DOVETAILS

$\frac{X}{2}$ X $\frac{X}{2}$

4 mm

T

SIDE ELEVATION

FRONT ELEVATION

PINS

$X \simeq \frac{2}{3}$ to $\frac{3}{4}$ T

N.B. GUIDE ONLY

Fig. 5.20 Proportioning a dovetail joint

THROUGH DOVETAIL

LAPPED DOVETAIL.

Fig. 5.19 Dovetail joints

Dovetail joints Figure 5.19 shows how dovetailing has been used to prevent members from being pulled apart. The strength of a dovetail joint relies on the self-tightening effect of the dovetail against the 'pins', as shown by the direction of the arrows.

Dovetail slope can vary between 1 in 6 to 1 in 8, depending on the physical hardness of the wood. The number of dovetails and their size will vary with the width of the board. The dovetails are usually larger than the pins (except those produced by machine – which are of equal width), and a guide to their proportions is given in fig. 5.20.

Figure 5.21 shows a method of marking and cutting a single through dovetail:

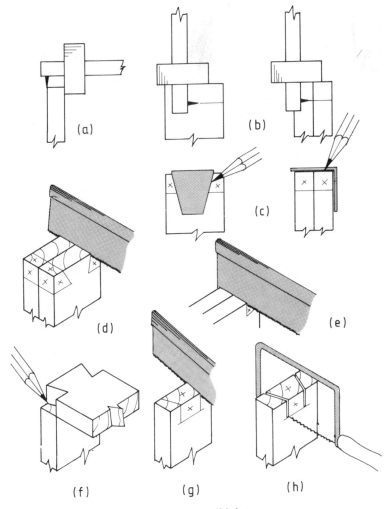

Fig. 5.21 Marking-out and cutting a dovetail joint

189

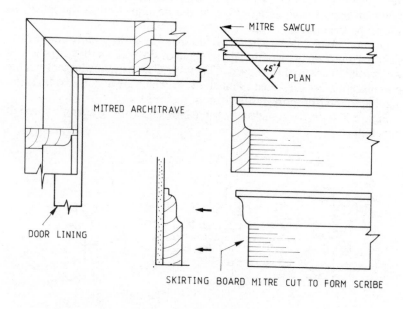

MITRE SAWCUT

PLAN

45°

MITRED ARCHITRAVE

DOOR LINING

SKIRTING BOARD MITRE CUT TO FORM SCRIBE

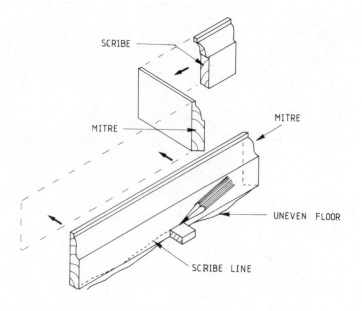

SCRIBE

MITRE

MITRE

UNEVEN FLOOR

SCRIBE LINE

Fig. 5.22 Mitre and scribe joints

a) Set the marking gauge to the material thickness.
b) Temporarily pin those sides (in pairs) which are to be dovetailed at their ends. Gauge all round.
c) Using a bevel or dovetail template, mark the dovetails (see fig. 2.12).
d) Cut down the waste side to the shoulder line, using a dovetail saw.
e) Cut along the shoulder line and remove the cheeks.
f) Divide the sides and mark off the pins.
g) Cut down to the shoulder line with a dovetail saw.
h) Remove waste with a coping saw, then pare square with a chisel.

The joint should fit together without any further adjustments!

Some joiners prefer to cut the pins first and the dovetails last. Both methods are acceptable, but the sequence described is quicker and tends to be more accurate.

Mitre and scribe joints These are generally associated with joining trims — i.e. cover laths, architraves, skirting boards, and beads — either at external or internal angles. The joint allows the shaped sections to continue round or into a corner, as shown in fig. 5.22.

A mitre is formed by bisecting the angle formed by two intersecting members and making two complementary cuts. A scribe joint has its abutting end shaped to its own section profile, brought out by first cutting a mitre (fig. 5.22). (See also volume 2 fig. 3.37 and volume 3 figs 3.5 and 6.14 for hand and machine scribes.)

Scribing Where a joint has to be made against an uneven surface, such as a floor, wall, or ceiling, scribing provides a means of closing any gaps. Figures 5.22 and 5.23 show that, by running a gauge line parallel to the uneven surface, an identical contour will be produced (see also fig. 2.5).

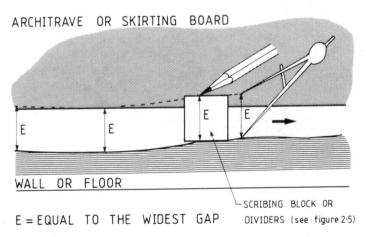

ARCHITRAVE OR SKIRTING BOARD

WALL OR FLOOR

E = EQUAL TO THE WIDEST GAP

SCRIBING BLOCK OR DIVIDERS (see figure 2·5)

Fig. 5.23 Scribing to an uneven surface

191

6 Suspended timber ground floors

As can be seen from fig. 6.1 this type of floor – also known as a 'hollow' floor – is made up of a series of timber beams, called 'joists', covered with boards. The whole floor is then supported by wallplates resting on purpose-built 'honeycombed' sleeper walls (figs 6.1 and 6.2). Alternatively, the joist ends can be built into the inner leaf of the perimeter cavity walls (fig. 6.3), provided they are protected from cavity moisture.

These floors have of recent years been the subject of many outbreaks of dry rot (see volume 2), primarily due to the timber used in their construction having been allowed to come into contact with sufficient amounts of moisture to raise its moisture content (m.c.) above the danger level of 20%. This problem can often be traced to the omission or breakdown of the d.p.c. (damp-proof course – a continuous layer of thin impervious material sandwiched between the brick or blockwork) which acts as a barrier against any rising damp. Alternatively, it may be due to moisture-laden air having been allowed to condense on the underside of the floor, due to inadequate ventilation of the subfloor space. Free circulation of air to the whole of the subfloor space is therefore essential, and is achieved by the provision of air bricks (purpose-made perforated blocks, fig. 6.2) in the outer perimeter walls and the honeycombing of sleeper walls. Dividing walls must also be strategically pierced.

Construction of these floors is strictly controlled by the Building Regulations 1985 to ensure both structural stability and protection against the ingress of moisture (fig. 6.2).

To achieve the correct overall balance in the design of the floor, the following factors covered by approved document A must therefore be taken into account:

a) clear span of joist,
b) joist sectional size,
c) joist spacing,
d) grade of timber to satisfy strength class (SC),
e) dead load supported by the joist,
f) flooring material,
g) flooring-material thickness.

6.1 Floor joists
The floor design is usually such that the joist is laid to bridge the shortest distance between room walls. This distance may however be further

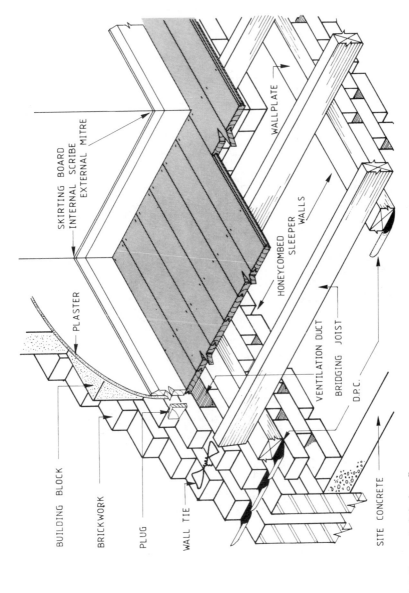

Fig. 6.1 Suspended timber floor

SKIRTING BOARD
INTERNAL SCRIBE
EXTERNAL MITRE

WALLPLATE

HONEYCOMBED
SLEEPER WALLS

PLASTER

VENTILATION DUCT

BRIDGING JOIST

D.P.C.

BUILDING BLOCK

BRICKWORK

PLUG

WALL TIE

SITE CONCRETE

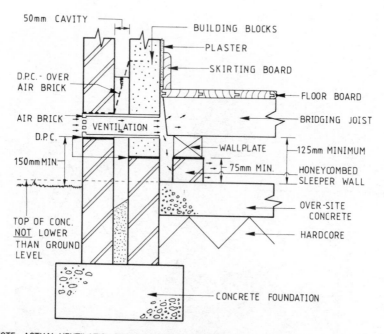

NOTE: ACTUAL VENTILATION OPENING TO EACH EXTERNAL WALL AT LEAST 300 mm² FOR EACH METRE RUN OF WALL

Fig. 6.2 Using sleeper walls to support floor joists

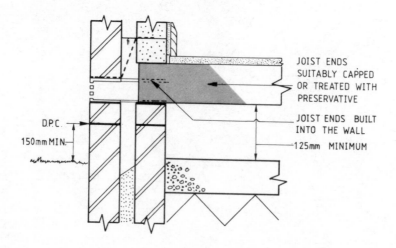

Fig. 6.3 Building-in floor joists (not recommended)

194

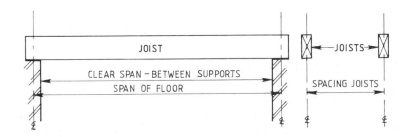

Fig. 6.4 Floor joist − span and spacing

reduced by the introduction of sleeper walls. The effective span of a
bridging joist is shown in fig. 6.4.

A joist end section in relation to its span must be strong enough not only
to withstand the dead weight of the floor but also safely to support any
load that may be placed upon it. The importance of stating timber sizes on
a drawing as *length × width × depth* (or *thickness*) should be stressed at
this point, particularly for those sections which are expected to withstand
heavy loads. Figure 6.5 shows the effect of dimensioning out of sequence.

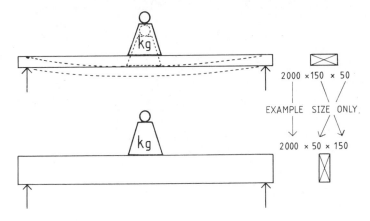

Fig. 6.5 Floor-joist end section in relation to its span

Joist spacing means the distance between the centres of adjacent joists,
as shown in fig. 6.4. These centres range between 400 and 600 mm,
depending on the factors previously stated. However, joist centres should
start and finish 75 mm in from the wall face (providing the joists are
50 mm wide). This will leave a 50 mm gap between the wall and the joist
running parallel to it, so allowing air to circulate freely.

Levelling

The levelling process can be carried out by one or a combination of the following methods:

a) spirit-level and straight-edge,
b) water (aqua) level (see volume 2, chapter 4),
c) optical levelling (see volume 2, chapter 4).

Figure 6.6 shows four simple stages that can be adopted with a spirit-level and straight-edge, provided there is sufficient room to work. If, however, restrictions prevent the joists from being sighted over, then use a spirit-level at stage 3 and a straight-edge to line through at stage 4. (A straight length of floor board will act as a suitable straight-edge.)

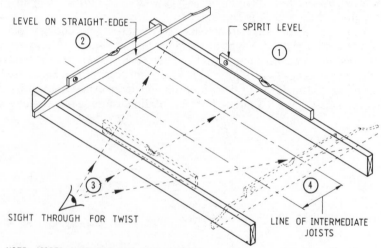

NOTE: JOISTS LAID CROWN (round) EDGE UP — ALLOWANCE MUST BE MADE WHEN LEVELLING AND SIGHTING THROUGH

Fig. 6.6 Laying and levelling floor joists

The accuracy of the whole process will depend very much on whether the wallplates (if used) were levelled correctly in the first instance. If the wallplates are level and the joists are all the same depth (regularised, fig. 6.7(a)) the bearing of the joists should only require minor adjustment.

If, however, it is found that adjustments must be made, figs 6.7(b) and 6.7(c) show acceptable methods. It should be noted that the method shown in fig. 6.7(d) will reduce the depth of the joist and therefore its efficiency over that span (see fig. 6.4).

The use of wallplates not only enables the floor's weight to be more evenly distributed over a wider area but also provides a means of securing the joists by nailing.

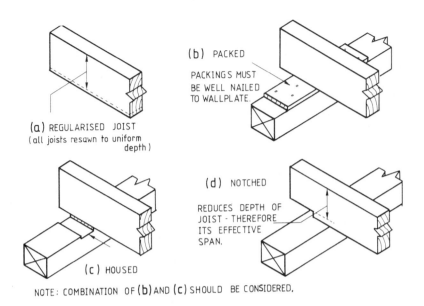

(a) REGULARISED JOIST
(all joists resawn to uniform depth)

(b) PACKED

PACKINGS MUST BE WELL NAILED TO WALLPLATE.

(c) HOUSED

(d) NOTCHED

REDUCES DEPTH OF JOIST - THEREFORE ITS EFFECTIVE SPAN.

NOTE: COMBINATION OF (b) AND (c) SHOULD BE CONSIDERED.

Fig. 6.7 Levelling and bearing adjustments

If the joist ends are to be built into the walls (fig. 6.3) it is advisable to use slate not wood as a packing, because the wood packing could shrink and eventually work loose. Alternatively, the method shown in fig. 6.7(d) may be adopted, provided the joist is deep enough to allow this method to be used without it being weakened. However, when the joists are level and correctly spaced, they must be kept that way by tacking a spacing lath on to the tops of the joists. This is removed after the joists have been walled in by the bricklayer.

6.2 Flooring (decking)
The flooring material will consist of either:

a) planed, tongued, and grooved (p.t.g.) floor board;
b) flooring-grade particle board (chipboard) — square-edged or tongued-and-grooved (see volume 2, chapter 6);
c) flooring-grade plywood — square-edged or tongued-and-grooved (see volume 2, chapter 6).

This volume deals with floor boards, whereas sheet flooring materials will be dealt with in volume 2.

Figure 6.8 shows a typical section of p.t.g. softwood board, with a deeper rebate cut from the upper face than from the underside. This deep rebate provides the joiner with a quick and useful guide to the board's face side. Also, before overall floor coverings (carpets etc.) became fashionable and less expensive, it was commonplace to walk directly on the floor boards — the only protection offered being a layer of varnish and/or wax

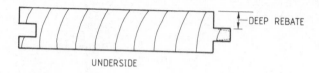

Fig. 6.8 Floor-board section

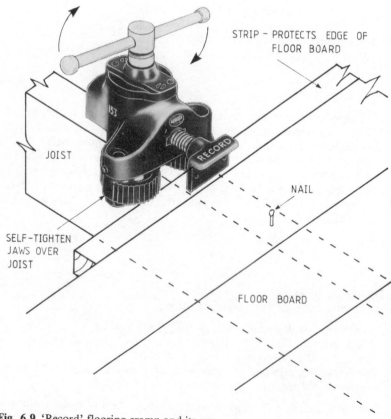

Fig. 6.9 'Record' flooring cramp and its use

polish. The story has it that the deeper rebate therefore allowed for more wear to take place before the tongue and grooves became exposed and the boards dangerously thin.

Laying floor boards

Boards are laid at right angles to the joists, and wherever they cross a joist they are eventually double-nailed to it — using either lost-head nails or flooring brads (section 14.1). Nails should be $2\frac{1}{2}$ times the thickness of the floor board, whereas flooring brads are of standard cut length.

The first board should be nailed approximately 15 mm away from one wall (the gap later being covered by skirting), then three to six boards are positioned edge to edge against it — the number of boards will depend on the method of clamping. Figure 6.9 shows a typical flooring clamp (cramp) and its application. In the past, lever and folding methods have been used (figs 6.10 and 6.11). Although not as efficient as the flooring clamps, these methods are still very effective and are useful when dealing with small areas or working in confined spaces. Once the boards have been cramped tight (not overtightened), they should be nailed to the joist or be spot nailed sufficiently to hold the boards in position.

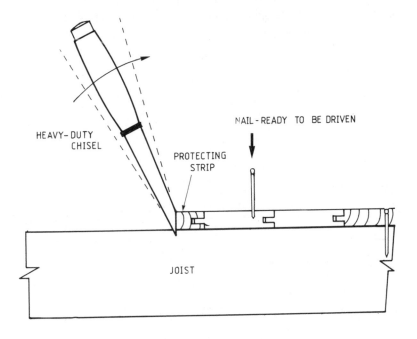

Fig. 6.10 Closing floor boards by leverage

199

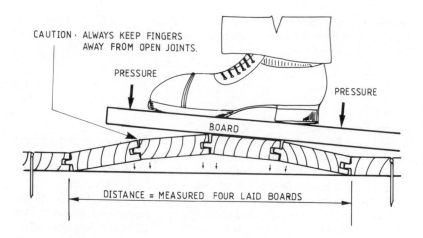

Fig. 6.11 Folding method of laying floor boards

Where the boards have to be end jointed, a splayed end joint can be used (fig. 6.12(a)). This helps to prevent splitting. These joints should always be staggered as shown in fig. 6.12(b) – not as fig. 6.12(c) – unless a trap has to be left in the floor for access to the subfloor space (fig. 6.13), in which case it should be sited in a non-traffic area, for example a cupboard under the stairs etc.

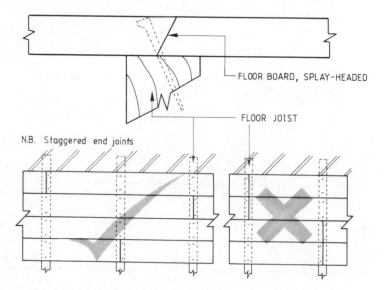

Fig. 6.12 End jointing of floor boards

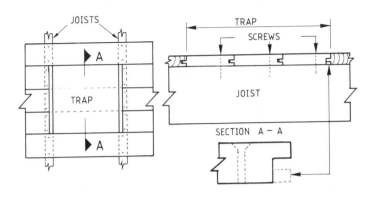

Fig. 6.13 Forming access and service traps

Continue in this way across the room, where the last few boards can be cramped using the methods shown in figs 6.10 and 6.11. The spot nailing should have been sufficient to indicate the centre position of *all* the joists, and this now enables the joiner to mark a series of pencil or chalk marks across the room as a guide for the final nailing-down process, followed by punching the nail heads just below the surface. (The final nailing-down process is often termed 'bumping'.) Using the spot-nailing method releases the flooring clamps for use in other rooms.

Note: if service pipes have been laid in close proximity to the floor joists, there is a danger of driving nails into them. It would therefore be advisable to nail that area fully as the floor boards are being laid, rather than trying to remember where the pipes were or forgetting to mark the danger area.

6.3 Skirting

After the plastering is complete, a set of new operations takes place − known as 'second fixing'. One of these operations is to fix the skirting-board.

Skirting-boards are machined to many different profiles, some of which are illustrated in fig. 6.14. The profile usually reflects the class of work being carried out.

The main function of a skirting-board is to provide a finish between the wall and floor. It also acts as a seal against draughts from the subfloor space and as a buffer to protect the wall covering from knocks that may occur during cleaning the floor covering − timber being much more resilient than plaster.

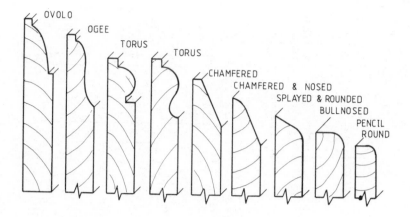

Fig. 6.14 Skirting-board sections

Fixing

Although skirting board is only a 'trim' (cover), because of its frequent ill-treatment it does require to be fixed firmly to the walls. This is usually achieved by one of three ways (see also chapter 14):

i) plugging (fig. 6.15(a)),
ii) timber grounds (figs 6.15(b) and 6.15(c)),
iii) direct nailing.

The use of wood plugs in brickwork is a very useful method of fixing to walls where brick or dense concrete blocks have been used. (Figures 14.7 and 14.8 show the method of preparing and fixing such plugs.)

Plastics plugs should also be considered as a modern alternative where fixing by screws is practicable or a permitted alternative (see chapter 14).

Figures 6.15(b) and 6.15(c) show the use of timber grounds as a fixing medium. The method of fig. 6.15(b) provides a finish for the plasterwork and a continuous longitudinal fixing, while leaving a narrow service duct behind the skirting; whereas that in fig. 6.15(c) is employed when used in conjunction with wall panelling.

Certain modern types of building blocks will permit nails to be driven directly into them, offering sufficient holding power for light-sectioned skirting-board, thus speeding up the whole fixing process.

Joints

There are only three joints to consider here:

i) butt joint,
ii) mitre joint (fig. 5.22),
iii) scribed joint (fig. 5.22).

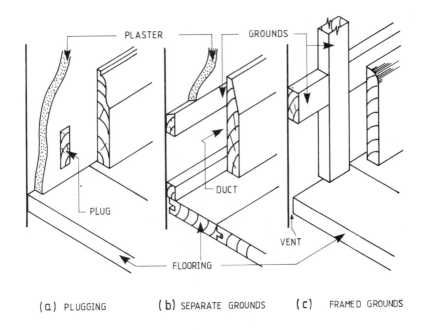

Fig. 6.15 Methods of fixing skirting boards to walls

The layout of the floor will dictate the position and type of joint employed. For example, at doorway openings it is common practice to butt the skirting board up to the door-casing trim (known as the architrave); external corners are mitred; and internal corners are scribed (figs 6.1 and 5.22). However, where a piece of skirting-board has to be joined in its length (a practice to be discouraged — it is not usually necessary), a cut of 45° is more desirable than a 90° butt joint. A cut of 45° enables the joint to be nailed more efficiently and provides a partial mask if or when shrinkage occurs (section 1.7).

The methods of cutting these joints is dealt with in section 5.3, together with the technique for scribing timber along its length — necessary where a skirting-board has to be fitted to an uneven floor surface (figs 5.22 and 5.23).

7 Gable-ended single roofs

The roof must be included in the design of a building as a whole, be it a factory, a house, or a garage. Just as its substructure depends on the roof for cover, so must the roof rely on the walls for support. Therefore the roof and walls must complement each other. Size, shape, location, use, and appearance are all factors which influence the choice of roof.

This chapter is concerned with roofs which span up to 4 metres, have surfaces steeper than 10° to the horizontal – known as 'pitched' roofs – and have their length terminated by end walls (gable walls).

7.1 Roof terminology

Figure 7.1(b) names those parts (elements) of a pitched roof to which the various members (components) shown in fig. 7.1(c) relate.

Single roof – common rafters span from wallplate to ridge board without intermediate support.

Double roof – common rafters have their effective span halved by mid support of a beam (purlin). Also known as a 'purlin' roof. (Discussed in volume 2.)

Roof span – usually taken as the distance between the outer edges of the wallplates (fig. 7.1(a)).

Roof rise – the vertical distance from a line level with the upper surfaces of the wallplates to the intersection of the inclined slopes (fig. 7.1(a)).

Roof pitch – the slope of the roof (fig. 7.1(a)) expressed either in degrees or as the fraction rise/span, i.e. rise divided by span. For example, for a rise of 1 m and a span of 2 m,

$$\text{roof pitch} \quad = \frac{\text{rise (1 m)}}{\text{span (2 m)}} = \frac{1}{2} \text{ pitch or } 45°$$

The roof covering, i.e. tiles, slates, etc., will determine the pitch to be used.

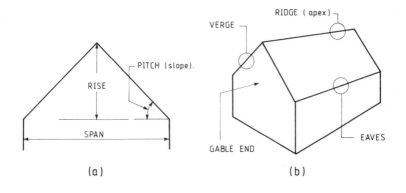

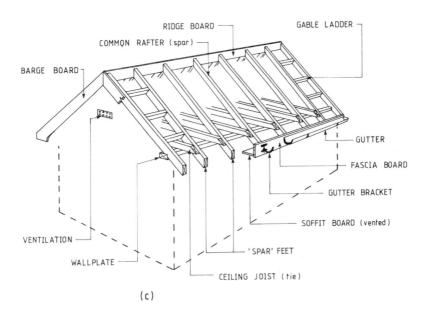

Fig. 7.1 Roof terminology

Roof elements (fig. 7.1(b))

Ridge (apex) – the uppermost part of the roof.

Gable – the triangular upper part of the end walls.

Verge – the overhanging edge at the gable ends.

Eaves – the area about the lower edge of the roof surface at the top of the outer face walls.

Roof components (fig. 7.1(c))

Ridge board − receives the ends of the rafters.

Common rafter (spar) − rafter spanning from wallplate to ridge board.

Gable ladder − framework taking the roof over the gable wall.

Ceiling joists − carry ceiling material and act as rafter ties.

Wallplate − provides a fixing for rafters and ceiling joists and distributes the roof load.

Barge (verge) board − cover (trim) for the ends of horizontal members, i.e. wallplate, gable ladder, and ridge board.

Fascia board − vertical facing to rafter ends (spar feet).

Soffit board − horizontal board closing the underside of the spar feet.

Gutter − channel section in metal, plastics, or wood fixed slightly off level to the spar feet to allow roof water to drain away to a fall pipe (downpipe). Wooden gutters are sometimes called 'eaves spouting'.

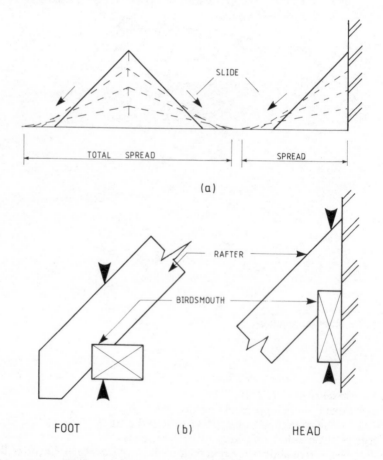

Fig. 7.2 The effect and restraint of an inclined rafter

7.2 Forming a pitched roof

If a length of timber was reared against a wall, like a rafter in a lean-to roof (fig. 7.4(b)), or leant against a similar inclined length to form the ridged effect of a couple roof (fig. 7.4(c)), it would become apparent that the slope, length, and weight, together with the smoothness of the surfaces in contact, would lead to the sliding effect shown in fig. 7.2(a).

Provided the rafters have bearings at the top and bottom of the roof which are capable of transmitting loads vertically, like those offered by monopitch and lean-to roofs (figs 7.4(a) and (b)), slide can be restrained by cutting a 'birdsmouth' into the rafter at these points — as shown in fig. 7.2(b). However, deflection (due to loading) of the rafters and the hinging effect at the apex of a couple roof could produce enough horizontal thrust to push the supporting walls outwards; therefore the walls must be strengthened or a tie be introduced into the roof structure.

These principles can be more fully understood by using a model similar to that shown in fig. 7.3(a). This consists of four narrow strips of plywood — two rafters, one tie, and a strut — with holes bored to suit either dowel or nuts and bolts (free to move). The walls are represented by short wide strips.

The arrangement can be set up as follows:

i) Figure 7.3(b) — when the pitch is varied, instability is very noticeable as the walls move away.

ii) Figure 7.3(c) — the introduction of a high collar (tie) produces severe bending of the rafters at this point. The walls still move outward.

iii) Figure 7.3(d) — when the collar (tie) is lowered, the roof slope becomes more stable (fig. 7.4(d)).

iv) Figure 7.3(e) — wall movement is prevented by fully lowering the tie (fig. 7.4(e)).

Figure 7.4 identifies common methods of forming pitched roofs and offers a guide to their maximum span. Size of members will depend on pitch, span, and form. Where a tie acting as a ceiling joist (couple close roof) exceeds 2.5 m, it will, for reasons of the most economical sectional size (see fig. 6.5), need to be restrained from sagging by using hangers and binders (fig. 7.4(f)); otherwise the sag will put undue stress on the joints and unbalance the framework.

7.3 Common rafters

Figure 7.5 shows a method of obtaining the bevels for common rafter 'plumb cut' and 'seat (foot) cut'.

A triangle is drawn to a suitable scale (the larger the better) to represent the roof's rise and half its span (to the outer edges of the wallplates) — fig. 7.5(a). The two angles formed by the common rafter are measured or transferred to a short end of timber by laying it over the drawing. The angles PC (plumb cut for common rafter) and SC (seat cut for common rafter) are clearly marked as shown in fig. 7.5(b). Rafter length is also

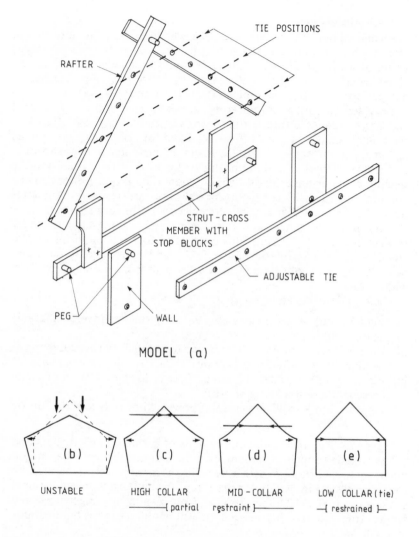

Fig. 7.3 Roof model, showing horizontal thrust

determined from the drawing and can be checked by using Pythagoras's theorem.

Using a sliding bevel, the angles are transferred to a full-size rafter (fig. 7.5(c)) which, when cut, is used as a pattern for all the other rafters – ensuring uniformity across the whole roof.

Note: in practice, the cut at X is made in-situ after the rafters are all assembled. This gives a certain amount of leeway if any adjustments have to be made.

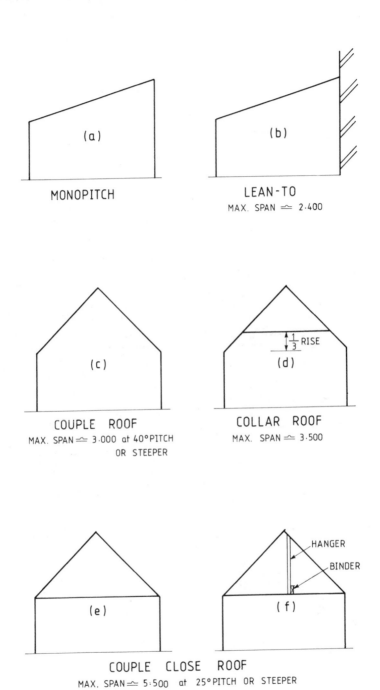

Fig. 7.4 Single roofs (pitched) for small spans

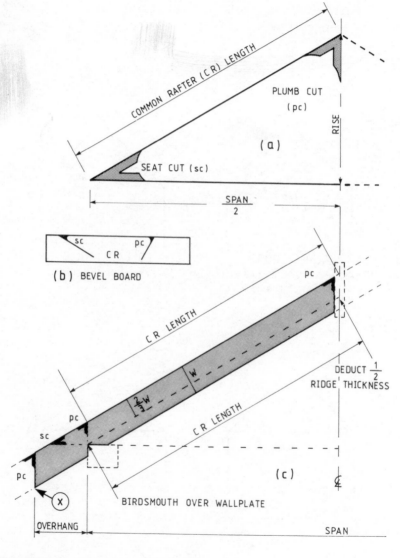

Fig. 7.5 Setting-out for a pattern rafter

7.4 Roof assembly

Listed below is a sequential guide to the assembly of a short-span gable-ended single pitched roof − to be used in conjunction with fig. 7.6.

1 *Wallplates*

    a) Assist the bricklayer to bed the wallplates and fix them straight, level, and parallel.

    b) Couple close roof − mark the positions of ceiling joists, taking into account that their centres should relate to the size of ceiling material (if used).

    c) Couple and collar roof − mark the positions of rafters.

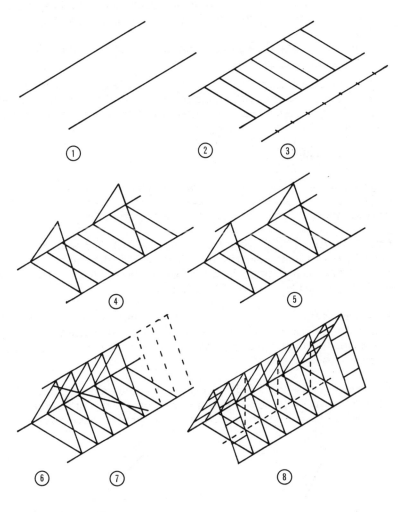

Fig. 7.6 Roof assembly

2 *Ceiling joists* Position and nail the ceiling joists to the wallplates – check that they are parallel.

3 *Ridge board* Mark the positions of rafters from the ceiling joists or wallplates.

4 *End rafters* Position and nail two end pairs of rafters to suit the length of the ridge (scaffolding must be used to suit the situation).

5 *Ridge* Position the ridge board (from underneath). Nail the ridge to the rafters and the rafters to the ridge at both ends.

6 *Intermediate rafters* Fix enough rafters to enable the roof framework to be plumbed and squared (the number required usually depends on the ridge-board length).

7 *Bracing* Plumb the roof from one gable wall and strap with a diagonal brace. Fix the remaining rafters to suit the ridge-board length.

8 *Gable ends* Mark the position and fix the gable ladder. Mark and fix binders and hangers if required.

If at any stage during the construction of a roof a person is liable to fall more than 2 metres, a working platform with suitable means of access must be provided and used, in accordance with the Construction Regulations 1966.

7.5 Eaves details

Flush eaves (fig. 7.7(a)) Spar feet are cut about 25 mm longer than the outer face wall, to allow for roof-space ventilation. Fascia boards are then nailed to them to form a trim and provide a bearing for gutter brackets.

Open eaves (fig. 7.7(b)) Spar feet are allowed to project well beyond the outer face wall. Fascia boards are often omitted, the gutter being supported by brackets fixed on the top or side of the spar ends. Eaves boards mask the underside of the roof covering.

Closed eaves (fig. 7.7(c)) Spar feet overhang but are completely boxed-in (provision must be made for ventilation). Purpose-made brackets will be required to support the soffit at the wall edge. The front edge can be tongued into the fascia.

Sprocketed eaves (fig. 7.7(d)) This is a method of reducing the roof pitch at the eaves of a steep roof, thus reducing the risk of water flowing over the gutter under storm conditions. The sprocket piece may be fixed on to or to the side of the rafter.

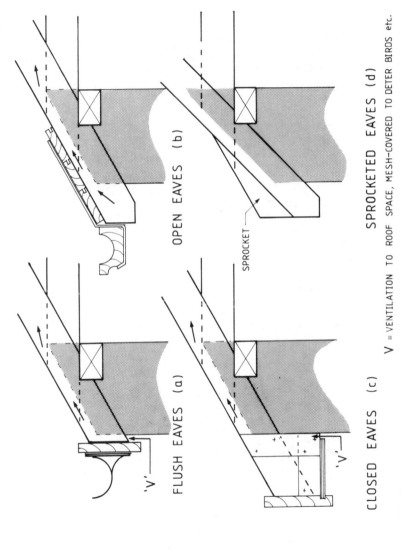

FLUSH EAVES (a)

OPEN EAVES (b)

CLOSED EAVES (c)

SPROCKETED EAVES (d)

SPROCKET

'V'

'V'

V = VENTILATION TO ROOF SPACE, MESH-COVERED TO DETER BIRDS etc.

Fig. 7.7 Eaves details

213

8 Turning pieces and centres up to 1 metre span

Where an opening is to be left in a wall as a passage, or to house a door or window frame, the load above it will need permanent support. A lintel (beam) can be used for this purpose, as shown in fig. 8.1(a), or an arch can be formed. Arches allow the load above them to be transmitted around their shape as shown in fig. 8.1(b).

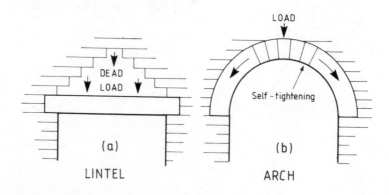

Fig. 8.1 Support above an opening

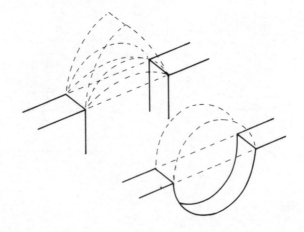

Fig. 8.2 Centres predetermine the shape of an opening

The construction of an arch necessitates substantial temporary support until it has set. A centre not only provides this support but also provides an outline of the arch on which the bricklayer lays his bricks or the mason his blocks. Several arch outlines are shown in fig. 8.2.

8.1 Simple geometrical arch shapes

Figures 8.3 to 8.7 illustrate methods of producing simple arch outlines. Arcs are scribed with the aid of a trammel bar and heads, as shown in fig. 2.6, or by similar improvised means.

Semicircular arch (fig. 8.3)

  i) Bisect AB to produce point C.
 ii) Using radius R (CA), scribe a semicircle from point C.

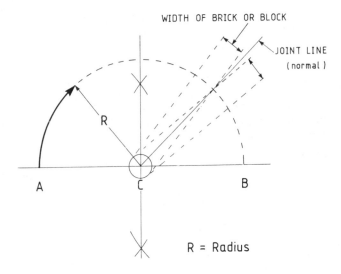

Fig. 8.3 Semicircular arch

Segmental arch (fig. 8.4)

   i) Bisect AB to produce a perpendicular line cutting AB.
  ii) Determine rise C.
 iii) Draw a line from A to C.
 iv) Bisect the chord AC to produce point D.
  v) Using radius R (DA), scribe an arc from A through C to B from point D.

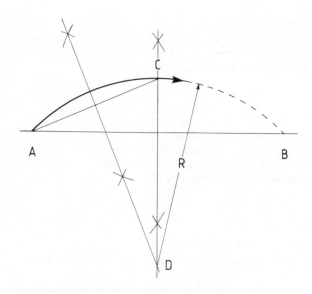

Fig. 8.4 Segmental arch

Equilateral arch (fig. 8.5)

i) Using radius R (AB), scribe the arc BC from point A.
ii) Similarly scribe arc AC from point B, point C being the intersection of both arcs.

Note: chords AC and BC will be the same length as span AB.

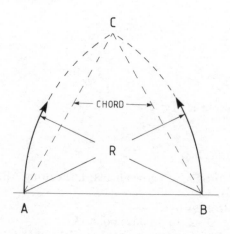

Fig. 8.5 Equilateral arch

Drop arch (fig. 8.6)

i) Bisect AB to produce a perpendicular line above AB.
ii) Determine rise C — but ensure that chord BC is shorter than line AB.
iii) Bisect chord BC to produce D on line AB.
iv) Using radius R (DB), scribe arc BC from point D. Use the same radius to obtain E, by scribing an arc from point A.
v) Arc AC is then scribed from point E.

Note: chords AC and BC will always be shorter than span AB.

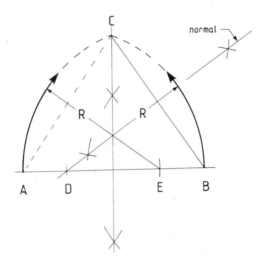

Fig. 8.6 Drop arch

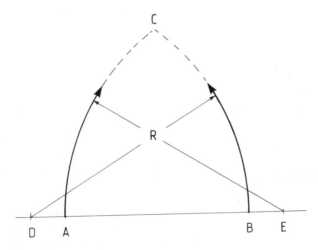

Fig. 8.7 Lancet arch

217

Lancet arch (fig. 8.7)

i) Using a distance longer than AB, scribe E on the base line from point A. Using the same distance, scribe D from point B.
ii) Use radius R (DB or EA) from points A and B to locate C.

Note: chords AC and CB will always be longer than span AB.

The method used to produce the lancet arch can also be used for the drop arch, and vice versa.

8.2 Turning pieces

A turning piece is used where the rise and span of the arch is small. It consists of a single length of timber with its top edge shaped to suit the soffit (under-side) of the arch — it acts as a temporary beam. Figure 8.8 shows a turning piece supported by props, with folding wedges as a means of adjustment, easing, and striking (see section 8.4).

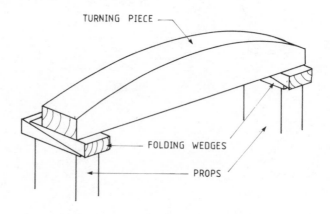

Fig. 8.8 Turning piece

8.3 Centres

Centres are wooden structures built-up of the following members:

Ribs form the profile of the arch and are made from sheet material (plywood) or solid sections joined with plywood or metal plates or are built-up of two thicknesses of timber with their joints lapping (see fig. 8.13). Ribs provide support and fixing for lagging.

Lagging — battens or plywood, nailed on to the ribs to form a platform for the walling material. Lagging is termed either 'closed' or 'open'. Open lagging has spaces left between battens and is used with large stone or blockwork.

Ties prevent built-up ribs from spreading and provide a fixing for bearers.

Struts stabilise the framework by helping to redistribute some of the load placed on the ribs.

Bearers tie the base of the centre and provide a sole, under which the centre is wedged and propped.

Note: all centres should be narrower than the wall thickness, otherwise they will hinder the bricklayer or mason when lining the wall through.

Construction
Start by drawing a full-size outline of half the centre. Remember to deduct the thickness of the lagging (except for centres for segmental arches) before setting out rib positions etc., as shown in fig. 8.9.

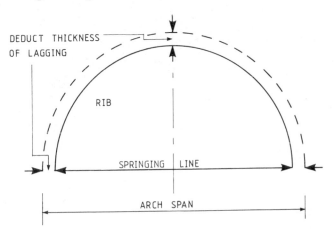

Fig. 8.9 Allowing for lagging

Figure 8.10 shows a centre suitable for a segmental arch and how its width can be increased by adding an extra rib. Plywood has been used as close lagging.

Figure 8.11 shows a semicircular centre with plywood ribs and timber noggins, bearers, and lagging.

By using two or more ribs for each outline, larger spans become possible and more economical. The way ribs are joined gives them their identity, as mentioned above. A 'solid' rib uses plated butt joints as shown in the centre for an equilateral arch (fig. 8.12).

219

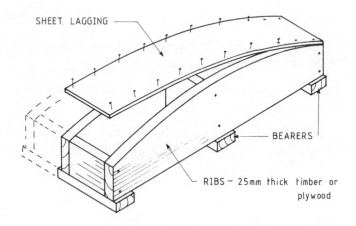

Fig. 8.10 Centre for segmental arch

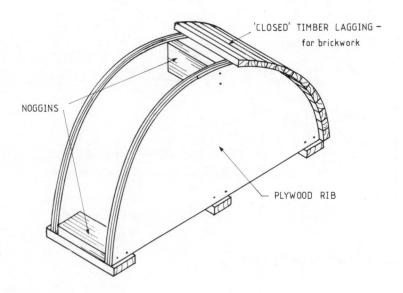

Fig. 8.11 Centre for semicircular arch

Figure 8.13 shows a centre with a built-up rib and how a rib pattern enables ribs to be cut economically. Patterns can be cut from hardboard or thin plywood.

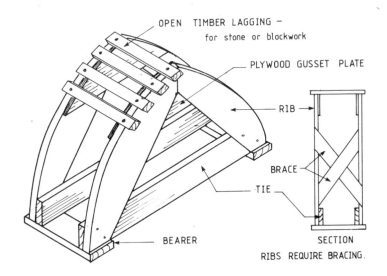

Fig. 8.12 Centre for equilateral arch

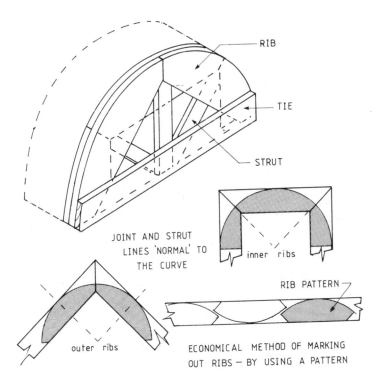

Fig. 8.13 Built-up rib construction

221

8.4 Easing and striking centres

Centres must be held in position without fear of their being displaced until the arch has thoroughly set, yet they must be capable of being gradually lowered. This lowering process, which takes place over a period of time, is known as 'easing'. Folding wedges allow the centre to be lowered slowly – any sudden movement could damage the arch. Methods of propping narrow and wide centres are shown in fig. 8.14. The eventual removal of the props and centre is known as 'striking' and is made easy by using folding wedges.

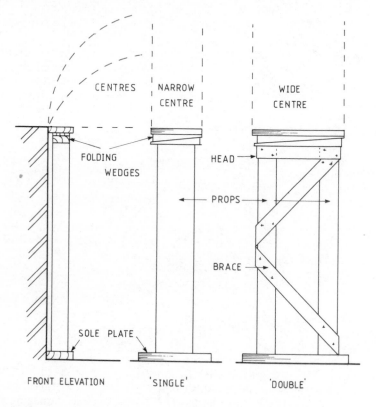

Fig. 8.14 Methods of propping

9 Formwork

Formwork is best described as a temporary construction designed to contain wet concrete until it has set. There are two distinct types of formwork:

a) *in-situ work (shuttering)* – where concrete is *cast in-situ* – that is to say, in the position it is to occupy;

b) *mould boxes* – used when concrete units are *pre-cast* by forming them in a mould, either at a convenient position on site or under factory conditions (often by a firm which specialises in concrete products) to be used as and when required.

9.1 Formwork design

Because wet concrete is a heavy semi-fluid plastic material, its formwork must be capable of restraining not only its mass but also its fluid pressure. The deeper the formwork, the greater the pressure it has to bear.

It is important to remember that the finished concrete surface will reflect the surface of its formwork. For example, sawn timber will produce a textured finish, just as planed timber, plywood (WBP), tempered hardboard, or sheet steel etc. will produce a smooth finish – provided their surfaces do not adhere to the concrete, which may be the case unless they are pre-treated with some form of parting agent or release agent. If a mould oil is used for this purpose, which also helps prevent air holes being left on the surface of the set concrete, its application must be strictly in accordance with the manufacturer's instructions.

For reasons of economy, formwork – particularly mould boxes – must be reused many times, therefore initial design must include quick, simple, and in some cases mechanical methods of assembly and striking (dismantling) without undue damage, by such means as wedges, bolts, cramps, and nails which can be easily redrawn without damaging the structure – preferably duplex-head types (Table 14.1).

The following items of formwork have been chosen for discussion because of their less complex nature. More advanced forms of formwork will be featured in volume 2.

9.2 In-situ work (shuttering)

The simplest forms are those which provide only side and/or end support, such as for a concrete drive, path, or base for a light garage or shed etc.

Figure 9.1 shows a simple layout of formwork for a concrete patio or greenhouse base — notice how a space has been left to one side to allow plants to be grown from the ground. Side boards are held by stakes firmly driven into the ground — packings between form board and stakes may be necessary where stakes are driven out of line. Stakes should be left long until the boards are fixed level. To avoid trapping encased boards, the corners have been cut back.

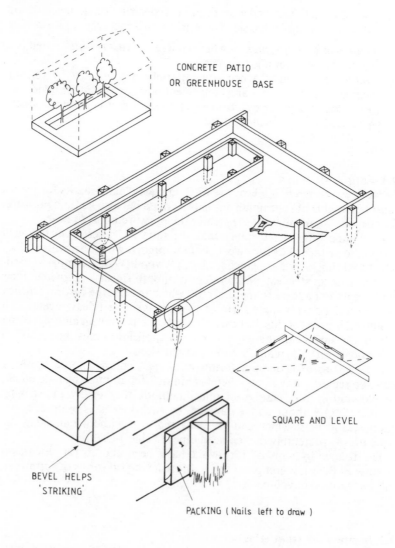

CONCRETE PATIO
OR GREENHOUSE BASE

SQUARE AND LEVEL

BEVEL HELPS
'STRIKING'

PACKING (Nails left to draw)

Fig. 9.1 Formwork for an in-situ concrete patio or base

9.3 Mould boxes

The shape of even a simple moulded object such as a jelly or a sand castle will hopefully reflect that of the mould from which it was produced. Similarly, concrete items such as those shown in fig. 9.2 should also accurately reproduce their moulds.

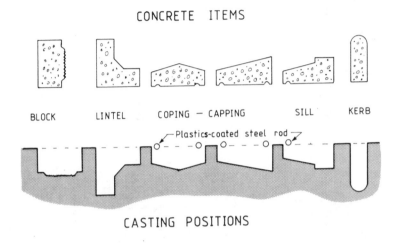

CONCRETE ITEMS

BLOCK LINTEL COPING — CAPPING SILL KERB

CASTING POSITIONS

Fig. 9.2 Common pre-cast concrete products

Because of the weight of their contents, or the need to cast several items together (fig. 9.3), mould boxes used for concrete products are usually made to dismantle easily.

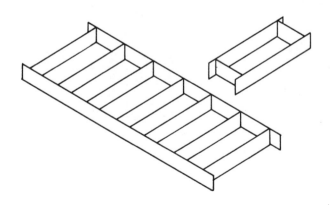

Fig. 9.3 Single and multiple casting units

225

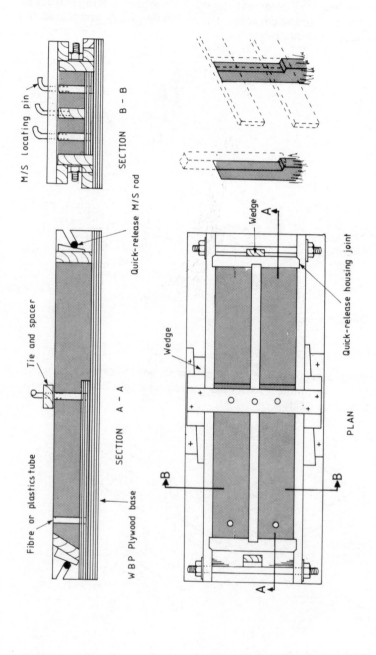

M/S locating pin

SECTION B - B

Quick-release M/S rod

Tie and spacer

SECTION A - A

Fibre or plastics tube

W B P Plywood base

Wedge

A

Wedge

Quick-release housing joint

PLAN

B

B

A

Fig. 9.4 Double mould box for pre-cast concrete posts

226

Figure 9.4 shows in orthographic projection how a double mould box could be constructed for a stump post, suitable for anchoring fence posts etc. to the ground. The holes in the post are formed by casting plastics or cardboard tubes into the concrete. Notice how the bolts which hold the box sides in position can be slid out without removing the nuts, and how the end-stop housings are bevelled for easy seating and removal.

The mould for a plant tub or litter bin shown in fig. 9.5 is kept intact, because the shape of its outer shell allows it to be lifted off, leaving the casting on the core mould until the concrete is cured (completely hardened).

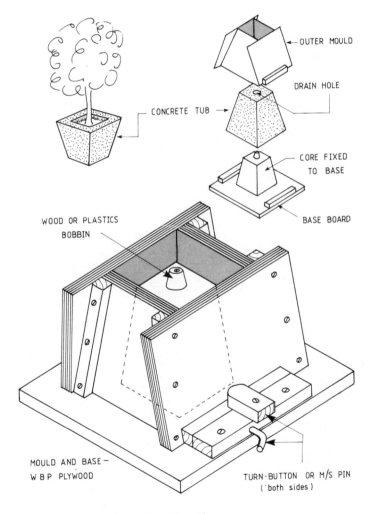

Fig. 9.5 Mould box for plant tub or litter bin

10   Ledged-and-braced battened doors

This type of door is commonly used as an exterior door to outhouses, sheds, garages (for pedestrian access), and screens. Provided it is made and fixed correctly, it will withstand a lot of harsh treatment and remain serviceable for many years.

10.1 Door construction

As can be seen from fig. 10.1, the face of the door is made up of V or beaded tongue-and-groove matchboard, known as 'battens'. These are nailed or stapled to three horizontal members called 'ledges', these ledges being held square to the battens by similarly fixing two diagonal pieces of timber called 'braces'.

A less expensive version of this door is the ledged-and-battened door. As its name implies, it is built without a brace − its stability therefore relies entirely upon its nailed contruction, which under normal circumstanes would prove inadequate. It can, however, be used quite satisfactorily in small openings or as a temporary door.

Door braces

The importance of a brace is illustrated in fig. 10.2(a), where it will be seen that its effectiveness is controlled by its direction: if the door is to retain its shape, the brace *must* always point away and in an upwards direction from the hanging side (hinged side), otherwise the door could sag at the closing side (fig. 10.2(b)) − hence the term 'sag bar' commonly used when referring to a brace.

The making of a simple card or wood model (fig. 10.3) should help to clarify bracing principles.

i) Cut four pieces of stiff card, thin plywood, or hardboard etc. 500 mm long by 50 mm wide to form the sides, top, and bottom.
ii) Join them together at the corners with a single pin, nail, or screw. This will allow each corner to pivot and produce a scissor movement.
iii) Lay the frame flat. Move the corners until they are square (at 90° to each other).
iv) Cut a piece of rigid material to fit between corners A and C − this will act as the brace.
v) While the brace is held in this position, take hold of side H. Lift the whole frame up and turn it until vertical. The brace should now be self-supporting, and therefore the frame will remain square. However, if the bracing piece had been omitted, or positioned into the

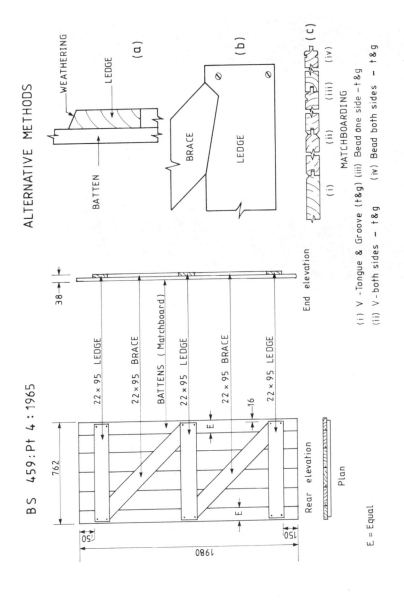

Fig. 10.1 Ledged-and-braced batten-door construction

BS 459:Pt 4 : 1965

ALTERNATIVE METHODS

(a)
WEATHERING
LEDGE
BATTEN

(b)
BRACE
LEDGE

(c)
MATCHBOARDING
(i) (ii) (iii) (iv)

(i) V - Tongue & Groove (t&g) (iii) Bead one side – t&g
(ii) V - both sides – t&g   (iv) Bead both sides – t&g

End elevation

38

22 × 95 LEDGE
22 × 95 BRACE
BATTENS (Matchboard)
22 × 95 LEDGE
22 × 95 BRACE
16
22 × 95 LEDGE

762

E

E

150

150

1980

Rear elevation

Plan

E = Equal

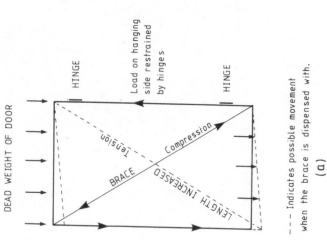

DEAD WEIGHT OF DOOR

HINGE

Load on hanging
side restrained
by hinges

HINGE

Tension

Compression

BRACE

LENGTH INCREASED

- - - Indicates possible movement
when the brace is dispensed with.

(a)

(b)

Fig. 10.2 Bracing principle

230

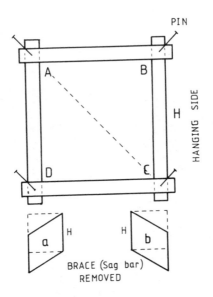

Fig. 10.3 Model to simulate frame movement

opposite corners B and D, the frame would have collapsed. In fact, corners B and D would have become wider apart (figs 10.3(a) and (b)), so allowing the brace to fall out.

BS 459:part 4:1965

Figure 10.1 shows some of the requirements specified by BS 459:part 4:1965 for the construction of a ledged-and-braced battened door, but it is worth noting that traditionally such doors have been and are still in some cases made from heavier sectioned timber and may also include other features such as those shown in fig. 10.1 − for example, weathering to ledges (bevelling on their top edge) where the door is subjected to weather from both sides (fig. 10.1 (a)), or extra brace restraint by housing braces into the ledges (fig. 10.1(b)).

10.2 Assembly

A typical order of assembly for a ledged-and-braced battened door is illustrated in fig. 10.4.

Stage 1

a) Cut the battens and ledges to length.
b) Check that the ledges are not twisted (plane them out of twist if necessary).

231

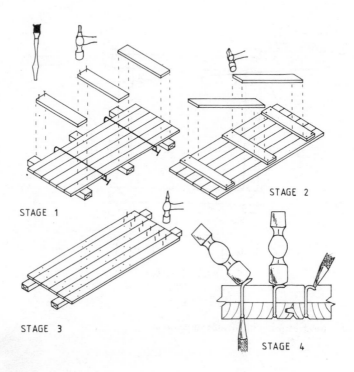

Fig. 10.4 Stages of door assembly

c) Paint or preserve all the tongues and grooves and the ledge faces that will come into contact with the battens.
d) Rest the battens face down across the bearers, then lightly cramp the battens together.
e) Double screw or nail each ledge to the cramped *edge* battens (fig. 10.5).

Stage 2

a) Cut the braces to fit between the ledges.
b) Edge nail the braces to the ledges (ensure that the door is kept square during this operation – if necessary, use end stops).

Stage 3

a) Turn the door over on to bearers which have been placed lengthwise.
b) Double nail each batten to the ledges and braces, taking care to avoid the bearers, as after the nails have been punched below the surface they will protrude 10 mm through the door.

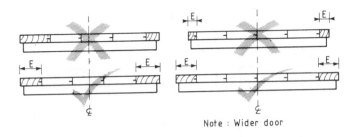

Note : Wider door

EDGE BATTENS MUST BE EQUAL (E) AND OF SUFFICIENT WIDTH
TO ALLOW FOR FIXING — ACHIEVED BY PLACING EITHER A
BATTEN OR JOINT TO THE CENTRE OF EACH LEDGE.

Fig. 10.5 Positioning edge battens

Stage 4

a) Turn the door back on to its face, where the protruding point of each nail will be visible.
b) Clench each nail, by bending it over in the direction of the grain, then punch the clench below the surface of the wood.

10.3 Framing

If the door is to be used to close an opening in a brick or block structure, a firmly fixed timber frame will be needed to support the door when hung (swung on hinges) and provide a means of making it secure.

The door frame will require a rebate to act as a door check, otherwise the door would swing through the opening, straining the hinge and/or splitting the jamb. Methods of forming a rebate can be seen in fig. 10.6(a). The width of the rebate will depend on whether the door is to swing outward or inward, i.e. whether the hinges are screwed directly on to the ledges or via the matchboard (fig. 10.6(b)).

Figure 10.7 deals with the making, assembly, and fixing of a suitable door frame. The head and jambs are joined together by using a mortise-and-tenon joint (figs 10.7(a) and (b)) which should be coated with paint or a suitable resin adhesive, assembled, cramped, wedged, and dowelled. If cramping the joint is not practicable, the joint could be draw-bored (fig. 10.7(c)) — when a hardwood dowel is driven through the off-centre holes, the shoulders of the joint will be pulled up tight. Because the frame has only three sides, a temporary tie (distance piece) fixed across the bottom of the jambs and a brace at each corner will be necessary if it is to retain its shape.

If the frame is to be built into the structure, temporary propping will be needed (fig. 10.7(d)). When the frame has been accurately posi-

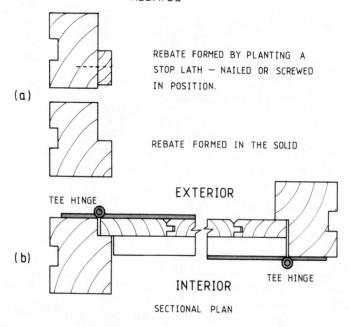

REBATES

REBATE FORMED BY PLANTING A
STOP LATH — NAILED OR SCREWED
IN POSITION.

(a)

REBATE FORMED IN THE SOLID

EXTERIOR

TEE HINGE

(b)

INTERIOR

TEE HINGE

SECTIONAL PLAN

N.B. Different width of rebate

Fig. 10.6 Forming rebates and positioning the door

tioned — both level and plumb — the permanent securing process can begin. Firstly, provision is made at the foot of each jamb for good anchorage to the step, either by using a metal dowel (fig. 10.7(e)) or shoe (fig. 10.7(f)) or a concrete stool (fig. 10.7(g)). As the walls are built up on either side, wall clamps are fixed at approximately 500 mm intervals with screws to the back of the jambs (fig. 10.7(h)), then walled in. On reaching the head (fig. 10.7(a)), it will be seen that the 'horns' or 'lugs' have been cut back on the splay. This allows the face walling to lap and totally enclose them, to make ready for the lintel above.

If, however, the frame is to be fixed into an existing opening, other fixing devices will have to be employed, for example wood or plastics plugs, wedges, etc. (see chapter 14). Specially formed openings should have built-in fixings — timber blocks (pallets) sandwiched between the mortar and courses of brick or blockwork, etc. Either way, it follows that the horns will not be needed as a fixing aid and they will therefore have to be sawn off. For greater stability, a haunched mortise-and-tenon joint is then used (fig. 10.7(b)).

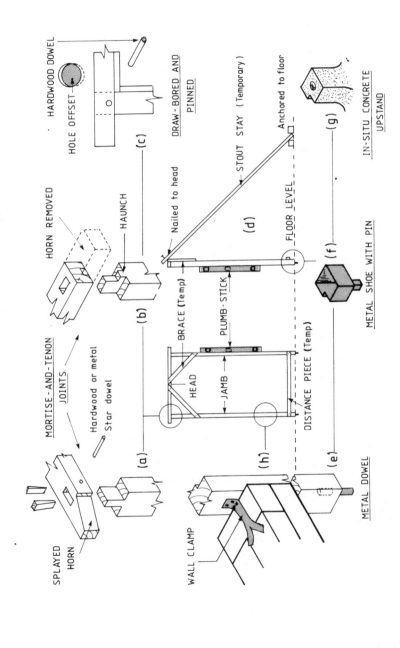

Fig. 10.7 Door-frame assembly and erection

235

10.4 Fitting and hanging

i) Check that the bottom of the door is parallel with the step or threshold – fit it if necessary.

ii) Fit the door's hanging edge into its rebate.

iii) a) (with an assistant) Position the door's hanging edge just inside its rebate. Using half the width of a pencil, scribe the closing edge – this will provide door clearance (fig. 10.8). Remove waste wood and bevel back to produce a 3 mm lead in – known as a 'leading edge'

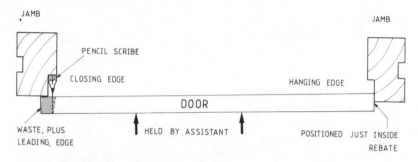

Fig. 10.8 Fitting the door to the closing edge

b) Alternatively, measure the distance between rebates (allowing for clearance), transfer it to the door's face, and remove waste wood as in (iii)(a).

iv) Place the door into the rebates, remembering to allow for floor clearance. Mark its height from inside the top rebate and remove waste wood.

v) Lay the door flat over two saw stools and screw tee hinges (fig. 10.9) to the battens or ledges, using only two screws per hinge.

vi) Position the door into its frame. Use thin wedges as packings and adjust to give clearance all round (2 to 3 mm at the sides and top, 4 to 6 mm to the floor). Fix the top hinge to the jamb, using only one screw, then the bottom likewise.

vii) Remove the packings. Check the clearance, noting any adjustments needed, and remedy if necessary.

viii) Repack the door. Unscrew the door from its frame – bottom hinge first – then remove both hinges from the door.

ix) Paint the backs of the hinges and refix them to the door, using *all* the screws this time.

x) Rehang the door and fix all the remaining screws.

Note: when using pre-painted hinges, stages (v) to (x) will not wholly apply.

Ironmongery

All that remains now is the choice of ironmongery to provide a way of keeping the door closed, e.g. a latch, lock, or bolt. The door's use, location, and accessibility will be the deciding factors here. If the door is simply to be held closed and to be opened from both sides, then a thumb latch would be an ideal choice. If, on the other hand, the door has to be fixed shut at some time, for security reasons, then the addition of a lock and/or bolt should be considered.

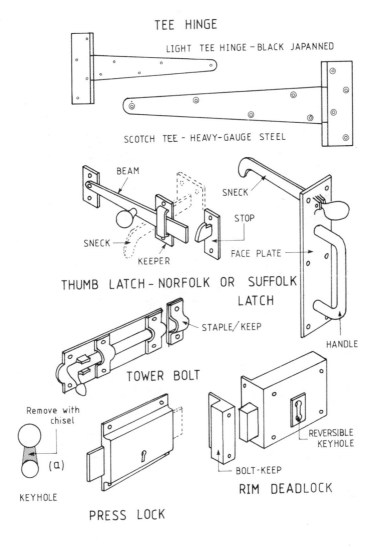

Fig. 10.9 Door ironmongery

Table 10.1 Sequence of operations for door construction

Process	Item	Member	Operation	Machines	Powered hand tools	Hand tools	Ironmongery	Remarks
Preparing timber	Door	Ledges, battens, braces	Cut to length, ripping, deeping.	Cross-cut circular-saw bench	—	—	—	Cut to nominal size – ex.
			Planing	Hand-feed planer/surfacer, panel planer/thicknesser	—	—	—	Finished size – width and thickness
		Battens	Form V, tongue and groove	Spindle moulder	Router	Rebate plane plough plane	—	Worked by machine or hand
Assembly	Door	Battens, ledges, braces	Fix battens to ledges		Staple gun	Hammer	Nails/staples	Paint or preserve T & Gs before assembly.
			Cut bevel and fix	—		Panel saw, hammer		
			Punch and clench nails			Hammer, nail punch		Boards held face to face during treatment.

238

Process	Item	Member	Operation	Machines	Powered hand tools	Hand tools	Ironmongery	Remarks
Finish	Door		Sanding	Belt sander sander	Belt/orbital sander	Cork sanding block, glass or garnet paper	—	Finish depends on grade of abrasive
	Door		Knotting Painting	—	—	Paint brush	—	Shellac knotting Priming paint

The thumb latch, sometimes known as a Norfolk or Suffolk latch, provides a simple yet trouble-free means of holding the door closed and should be fixed in the following manner:

i) Make a slot in the door, into which the sneck is pushed.
ii) Screw the face-plate (to which the sneck is hinged) to one face of the door.
iii) Fix the beam and keeper to the opposite side.
iv) The stop can now be screwed to the frame.

Note: black japanned round-headed screws should be used throughout.

Probably the simplest way of making the door secure is by the use of a tower bolt, screwed to the door's ledge. A press lock or rim deadlock will require a keyhole to be made in the door (fig. 10.9(a)).

10.5 Items and processes

An overall sequence of operations can be listed in chart form as an easy means of reference. Table 10.1 shows how the door's construction can be tabulated.

11   Single-light casement windows

The main purpose of a window is to allow natural light to enter a building yet still exclude wind, rain, and snow. It also serves as a means of providing ventilation if the glazed area is made to open. An openable 'light' (a single glazed unit of a window) is called a 'sash' or 'casement' − hence the term 'casement window'.

Figure 11.1 shows details of two types: the 'traditional', which houses its sash fully within its frame, and the more modern 'stormproof' type which, because of its double-rebate system − i.e. both the frame and the sash are rebated − gives better weather protection and increased natural light. Because the rebate in the frame of the 'stormproof' type is only half the sash width, direct glazing (a deadlight) can be incorporated into the frame.

11.1 Construction

Construction methods will depend mainly on the type of window and the sectional profile of its members. Traditional sections (and stormproof sections to BS 644) are shown in detail in fig. 11.1. Modified sections used in 'Crosby' windows, made by Crosby & Co. Ltd (fig. 11.2), show how sections have developed in recent years. The important feature of all these sections is how the grooves are formed to provide protection against the entry of moisture by capillary action (see chapter 12).

Window frames

Frames should be held together at the corners with either combed joints (multiple corner bridles) with not less than two tongues, or mortise-and-tenon joints. The tongues or tenons should be not less than 12 mm in thickness. Where lugs or horns are required for building-in purposes, they should not be less than 40 mm in length. Joints should be glued, with a suitable synthetic adhesive, and be held by wedges and/or pegged with hardwood or metal star dowels.

Casements (sashes)

The corners should be joined by using combed or mortise-and-tenon joints, glued (as above), and pegged and/or wedged (depending on the type − bridle joints cannot be wedged).

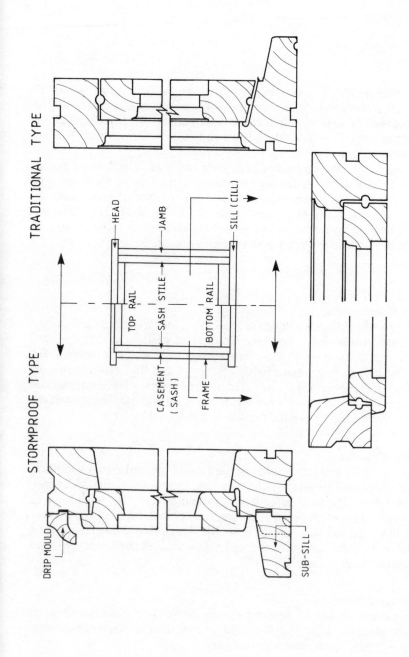

Fig. 11.1 Sectional details of single-light casement windows

TRADITIONAL TYPE

STORMPROOF TYPE

HEAD

JAMB

SILL (CILL)

TOP RAIL

SASH STILE

BOTTOM RAIL

CASEMENT (SASH)

FRAME

DRIP MOULD

SUB-SILL

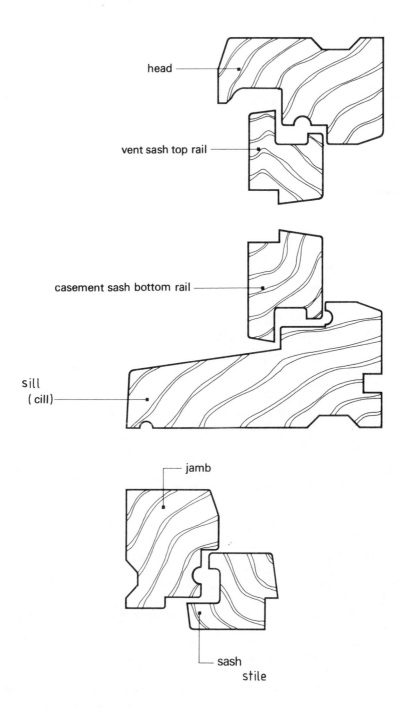

Fig. 11.2 The 'Crosby' metric D.C. window

243

Sash hanging

Sashes can be hung in one of the three ways shown in fig. 11.3, where the apex of the 'V' indicates the hinging side and that the knuckle (fig. 11.4) of the hinge is to that face. Three different types of hinge are shown in fig. 11.4, together with their respective fixing details.

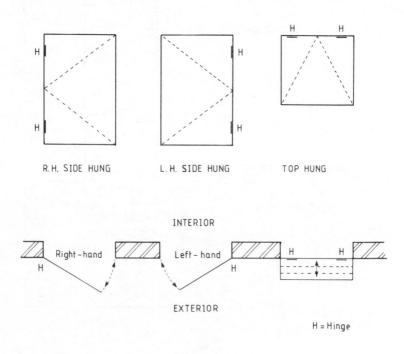

Fig. 11.3 Opening casements (handed from interior)

The screws used to fix the hinges will be exposed to varying amounts of strain, particularly those used on the top hinges of side-hung sashes, and those on sashes which are top hung which will constantly be subjected to 'withdrawal'.

Because openable sashes must provide varying amounts of ventilation, a multi-position casement stay similar to the one shown in fig. 11.4 is used. This also gives a means of securing the sash when closed. Side-hung sashes also use a window fastener (fig. 11.4) fixed midway to the closing-side stile and jamb.

Glass is not usually fixed until the window is built into the structure, but its weight must be taken into account with regard to hinge and screw sizes. The glass also plays an important part in holding the sash square.

244

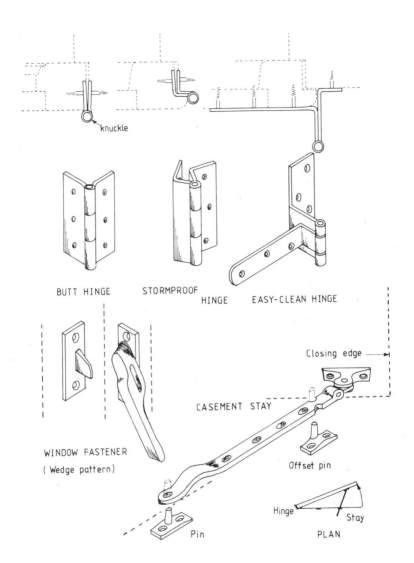

knuckle

BUTT HINGE   STORMPROOF HINGE   EASY-CLEAN HINGE

WINDOW FASTENER
(Wedge pattern)

CASEMENT STAY

Closing edge

Offset pin

Pin

Hinge   Stay

PLAN

Fig. 11.4 Window ironmongery

11.2 Fixing to the structure

Window frames can either be built into the fabric of the structure as building progresses, in a similar manner to the door frame shown in fig. 10.7, or be fixed with screws and plugs into a pre-formed opening after the main structure is built. The former is the most common method used in house building.

Figure 11.5 shows a vertical section of how a typical window unit is incorporated into the main outer fabric of a house.

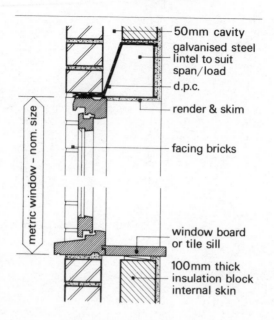

Fig. 11.5 The 'Crosby' window installation details

12 Moisture movement

One of the main requirements in building a habitable dwelling is that moisture be excluded from its interior — failure to do so could result in a high moisture content of timber and its eventual breakdown by moisture-seeking fungi, not to mention the many other structural and environmental effects associated with dampness.

Most building materials are porous (contain voids or pores), thus allowing moisture to travel into or through them. Moisture may enter these materials from any direction, even the underside and travel upwards as if defying the laws of gravity.

Upward movement of moisture is responsible for rising damp and is caused by a force known as a 'capillary' force which in the presence of surface tension produces an action called 'capillarity'.

12.1 Surface tension

The microscopic molecules of which water is composed are of a cohesive (uniting or sticking together) nature which, as a result of their pulling together, produces the apparent effect of a thin flexible film on the surface of water. This effect is known as 'surface tension'.

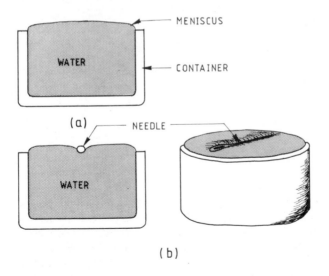

Fig. 12.1 The effect of surface tension

The reluctance of this 'skin' to be broken can be seen by filling a container with water just below its brim, then slowly adding more water until a meniscus (curved surface of liquid) has formed (fig. 12.1(a)). Its elasticity can be demonstrated further by carefully floating a small sewing needle or a thin flat razor blade (double-edged safety-razor type) on its·surface. Figure 12.1(b) shows how a depression is made in the 'skin' by the weight of a needle. If, however, surface tension is 'broken' by piercing the 'skin', the needle will sink.

12.2 Capillarity

A clear clean glass container partly filled with water will reveal a concave meniscus where the water has been drawn up the sides of the glass (fig. 12.2(a)). This indicates that a state of adhesion (molecular attachment of dissimilar materials) exists between the glass and water molecules and at this point is stronger than the cohesive forces within the water.

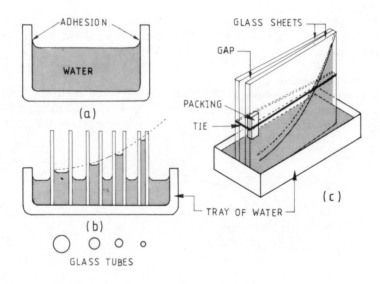

Fig. 12.2 The effect of capillarity

Figure 12.2(b) shows what happens when a series of clean glass tubes is stood in a container of water. The water rises highest in the tube with the smallest bore (hole size), indicating that the height reached by capillarity is related to the surface area of water in the tube. It can therefore be said that, if the surface area of water is reduced or restricted, the downward pull due to gravity will have less effect, whereas upward movement will be encouraged by surface tension.

248

A similar experiment can be carried out by using two pieces of glass as shown in fig. 12.2(c). This method produces a distinct meniscus which can be varied by making the gap at the open end wider or narrower.

It should now be apparent that, for a capillary force to function, all that is needed is water with its cohesive properties and a porous material, or a situation providing close 'wettable' surfaces which encourage adhesion.

12.3 Preventative measures

A knowledge of how water acts in certain situations and reacts towards different materials enables a building and its components to be designed with built-in water and moisture checks. For example, the common method of preventing moisture from rising from the ground into the structure is by using a horizontal damp-proof course (d.p.c.) like those shown in fig. 6.1, where penetrating damp has also been avoided by leaving a 50 mm cavity between outer and inner wall skins. A vertical d.p.c. would be used where both skins meet around door and window openings.

There are, however, many other places – particularly the narrow gaps left around doors and sashes – which would provide ideal conditions for capillary action if preventative steps were not taken. The first line of defence should be to redirect as much surface water away from these areas as possible, by recessing them back from the face wall and encouraging water to drip clear of the structure.

Figure 12.3 shows how a 'throat' (groove) cut into the underside of overhangs – i.e. thresholds, window sills, drip moulds, etc. – interrupts the flow of water by forcing it to collect in such a way that its increase in weight results in a drip being formed. Further examples of throatings are shown in figs 11.1, 11.2, and 11.5

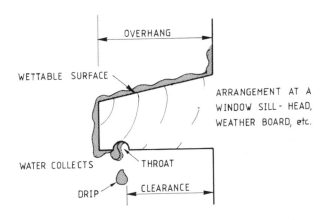

Fig. 12.3 Encouraging water to drip

It is inevitable that water will find its way around those narrow gaps, so anti-capillary grooves, or similar, are used. Figure 12.4 shows how these grooves work, and figs 11.1 and 11.2 illustrate how they are included in window design.

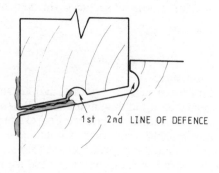

1st 2nd LINE OF DEFENCE

Fig. 12.4 Anti-capillary grooves

13   Shelving

Shelves are expected to support the differing weight-to-volume ratios of a vast variety of items and materials. It is therefore essential that, before shelves are constructed or assembled, consideration is given to both their function and location, because these are the essential factors that must be integrated within the overall design.

Figure 13.1(a) shows the dangers of

i) using shelving of inadequate thickness or strength to withstand the necessary imposed loads, or
ii) expecting shelving to span an unrealistic distance.

Figures 13.1(b) and (c) can be regarded as suitable remedial alternatives, i.e. providing the necessary intermediate support and/or using stronger material.

Shelves are made up of either 'solid' or slatted material, and examples are shown in fig. 13.2 (see also section 5.2).

Over the years, various methods of supporting shelves have evolved which the joiner can adapt to suit his specific requirements. A few

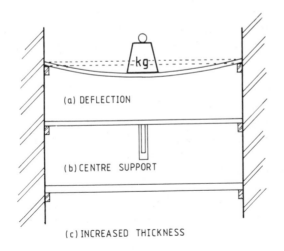

(a) DEFLECTION

(b) CENTRE SUPPORT

(c) INCREASED THICKNESS

Assume shelf end supports are adequate

Fig. 13.1 Shelf support

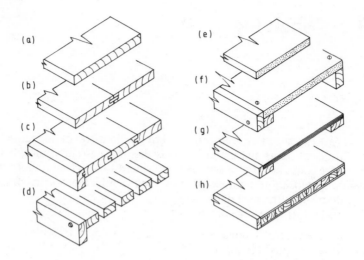

Fig. 13.2 Shelf boards and their construction: (a) single board; (b) double board with loose tongue; (c) tongued-and-grooved boards with front stiffener; (d) slatted with front stiffener; (e) particle board − self finish or with veneered wood or plastics; (f) particle board with front and back stiffeners; (g) plywood with front stiffener and back support; (h) blockboard or laminboard with slipped front edge

examples of these methods will be found in sections 13.1 and 13.2. You should also consult chapter 14 with regard to fixing devices.

13.1 Traditional shelving

As can be seen from fig. 13.3, shelves can be supported by

a) bearers fixed to a wall;
b) brackets − metal, or purpose-made from timber and/or plywood;
c) timber-framed uprights (standards);
d) solid uprights (enclosed units), where provision for shelf adjustment can be made.

The methods in figs 13.3(a) and (b) rely on walls for their support, whereas those in figs 13.3(c) and (d) may be free-standing units.

13.2 Proprietary systems and shelving aids

Commercially produced forms of shelf support may follow a similar pattern to those in figs 13.3(b) and (d) but provide for greater flexibility, in both their construction and the means of shelf adjustment.

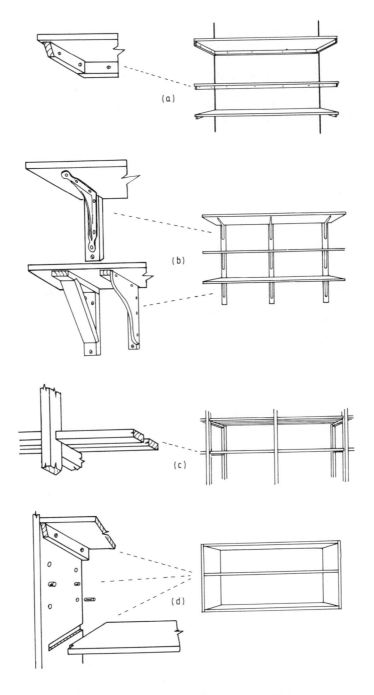

Fig. 13.3 Traditional methods of shelf support and assembly

Figure 13.4(a) shows how metal brackets of various styles and sizes can be positioned to any height by hooking them on to an upright metal channel which has been secured to a wall. Figure 13.4(b) shows how a series of holes bored in a solid upright enables metal or plastics shelf-supporting studs and their sockets to be positioned to suit shelf requirements. Alternatively, a metal strip can be housed or surface-fixed with adjustable pegs as shown in fig. 13.4(c).

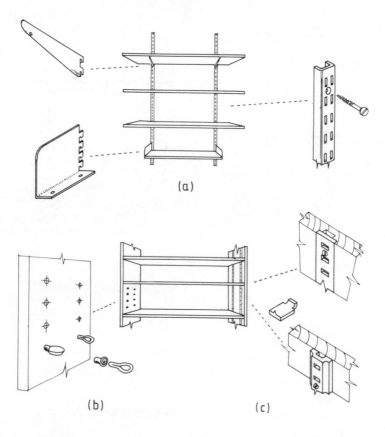

(a)

(b)   (c)

Fig. 13.4 Proprietary methods of shelf support

Conclusion Stop for a moment to consider how shelves are utilised around your home and place of work, then ask yourself: are they suitable for the job they are doing? are they strong enough? should they be wider or higher? are the method of construction and the shelf material in keeping with their surroundings? etc. From your answers, you should be able to draw your own conclusion as to the importance of this chapter.

14   Fixing devices

The decision as to how a piece of timber is fixed and which device to use is usually left to the joiner — unless the designer states otherwise. In either case, the following factors should be considered:

a) location,
b) strength requirements,
c) resistance to corrosion,
d) appearance,
e) availability,
f) cost.

14.1 Nails
Nails offer the quickest, simplest, and least expensive method of forming or securing a joint and, provided the material being fixed is suitable and the nails are the correct size (length approximately $2\frac{1}{2}$ times the thickness of the timber being fixed), the correct shape, and correctly positioned to avoid splitting, a satisfactory joint can be made.

Table 14.1 illustrates different types of nails, pins, and staples and describes their common use.

Key to Tables 14.1 to 14.4

Materials
A – aluminium alloy   B – brass   BR – bronze   C – copper
P – plastics   S – steel   SS – stainless steel

Finish/treatment
B – brass   BR – bronze   CP – chromium   G – galvanised
J – japanned (black)   N – nickel   SC – self-coloured
SH – sherardised   Z – zinc

Head shape
CKS – countersunk   DM – dome   RND – round head
RSD – raised head   SQ – square

Drive mechanism
SD – Superdriv (Posidriver)   SL – slotted (screwdriver)
SP – square head (spanner)
(Note: 'Superdriv' is the successor to 'Posidriv'.)

Table 14.1 Nails, pins, and staples

Nail type	Material	Finish or treatment	Shape or style	Application
Nails				
Round plain-head wire	S	SC		Carpentry; carcase construction; wood to wood
Clout (various sized heads)	S, C	SC, G		Thin sheet materials; plasterboard; slates; tiles; roofing felt
Round lost-head wire	S	SC		Joinery; flooring; second fixing. (Small head can easily be concealed.)
Oval lost-head wire	S	SC		Joinery; general-purpose. Less inclined to split grain.
Improved nails				
Twisted shank	S	SC, G		Roof covering; corrugated and flat materials, metal plates, etc.; flooring; sheet materials. Resist
Annular-ring shank		SH		popping (lifting). Good holding power, resisting withdrawal.
Duplex head	S			Where nails are to be re-drawn – formwork etc.
Flooring brad (cut nail)	S	SC		Floor boards to joists (good holding-down qualities)

Nail type	Material	Finish or treatment	Shape or style	Application
Panel pins Flat head Deep drive	S	SC, Z G	○ ○	Beads and small-sectioned timber Sheet material; plywood; hardboard
Masonry nails	S/hardened and tempered	Z	○	Direct driving into brickwork, masonry, concrete. (Caution: not to be driven with hardened-headed hammers. Goggles should always be used.)
Staples (mechanically driven)	S	Z	TEMPORARILY BONDED	Plywood Fibreboards Plaster-boards Insulation board to wood battens
Corrugated fasteners ('dogs')	S	SC	JOINT	Rough framing or edge-to-edge joints
Star dowel	A	SC	✛	An alternative to hardwood dowel for pinning mortise and tenons or bridles

When dismantling a joint or fixture which has been nailed, pay particular attention to the effort required to withdraw the nail, and whether the head pulls through the material. The ease or difficulty of withdrawal emphasises the importance of choosing the correct nail for the job. Apart from the nail size or type of head, resistance to withdrawal could be due to the following:

a) type of wood;
b) rust and pitting (fig. 14.1(a));
c) surface treatment of the nail, e.g. rough (fig. 14.1(b)) or galvanised etc.;
d) nail design, i.e. improved nails (fig. 14.1(c));
e) dovetail nailing (fig. 14.1(d)).

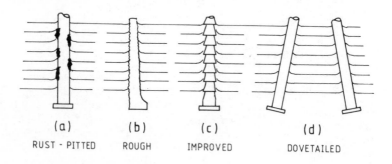

| (a) | (b) | (c) | (d) |
| RUST - PITTED | ROUGH | IMPROVED | DOVETAILED |

Fig. 14.1 Nails – resistance to withdrawal

Nails are more commonly associated with joints which require lateral support – preventing one piece of timber sliding on another. Nails in this instance are providing lateral resistance (see fig. 14.2), and, for this to be sustained, resistance to withdrawal is vital.

When nailing wood, splitting can be a problem and can occur when

i) nailing too near to the edge or end of a piece of timber;
ii) the nail gauge is too large for the wood section (especially small sections of hardwood);
iii) nailing one nail behind another in-line with the grain;
iv) using an oversized nail punch;
v) trying to straighten bent nails with a hammer.

If the above cannot be resolved by using other types or sizes or repositioning, then the following remedial measures could be considered:

a) remove the nail's point – N.B. this reduces holding power;
b) pre-bore the timber being fixed;
c) use oval nails;
d) use lost-head nails;
e) remove bent nails – bent nails never follow a true course.

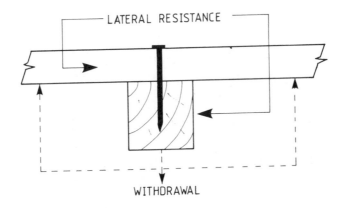

Fig. 14.2 Nails — lateral resistance

14.2 Wood screws

Wood screws have a dual function — not only do they hold joints or articles together; they also act as a permanent cramp, which in most cases can be removed later for either adjustment or modification purposes.

There is a vast variety of screws on the market, and knowing the correct type, size, or shape to suit a specific purpose will become a valuable asset to the joiner. Table 14.2 illustrates several wood-screw fixing devices, together with their use and driving methods. Screw cups and domes (used to conceal yet still provide access to the screw head) are shown in Table 14.3.

Wood-screw labels serve as a quick method of identification, combining an abbreviated description with a screw silhouette or head style and a colour code which represents its base metal (except orange which signifies 'Twinfast' screws). Figure 14.3 shows a typical example of a screw label.

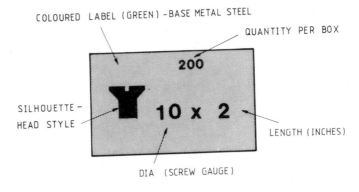

Fig. 14.3 Wood-screw label identification

259

Table 14.2 Wood-screw fixing devices

Screw type	Material	Finish/ treatment	Head shape/style	Drive mechanism	Application
Wood screw	S, B, BR, A, SS	B, BR, CP, J, N, SC, SH, Z	CKS, RND, RSD	SL, SD	Wood to wood; metal to wood, e.g. ironmongery, hinges, locks, etc.
Twinfast wood screw	S, SS	B, SC, SH, Z		SD only	Low-density material: particle board, fibreboard, etc. Drive quicker than conventional screws, having an extra thread per pitch for each turn.
Coach screw	S	SC, Z	SQ	SP	Wood to wood; metal to wood (Extra-strong fixing)
Clutch screw	S	SC			Non-removable – ideal as a security fixing
Mirror screw	S, B	CP	CKS, DM		Thin sheet material to wood – mirrors, glass, plastics

Screw type	Material	Finish/ treatment	Head shape/style	Drive mechanism	Application
Dowel screw (double-ended)	S	SC			Wood to wood – concealed fastener, cupboard handle, etc.
Hooks and eyes	S	B, CP, SC			Hanging – fixing wire, chain, etc.

Table 14.3 Screw cups and caps

	Screw cups	Cover domes
Material Finish/colour Shape	B, SS SC, N	P Black, white, brown
Application	Countersunk flange increases screw-head bearing area. Used where screw may be re-drawn, e.g. glass beads, access panels, etc.	(a) slots over screw; (b) slots into screw hole; (c) slots into Superdriv screw head. Neat finish yet still indicates location.

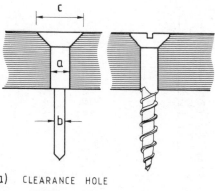

(a) CLEARANCE HOLE

(b) PILOT HOLE

(c) COUNTERSUNK

Fig. 14.4 Preparing material to receive a wood screw

Figure 14.4 shows how materials should be prepared to receive screws, namely by boring

a) a clearance hole to suit the screw shank,
b) a pilot hole for the screw thread,
c) a countersink to receive the screw head − if required.

A bradawl can be used to bore pilot holes in softwood. Failure to use pilot holes could result in the base material splitting and/or losing holding power.

14.3 Threaded bolts
For the purpose of quick reference, Table 14.4 illustrates those bolts which the carpenter and joiner is likely to encounter. Probably the most common of these is the coach or carriage bolt, and figs 14.5(a) and (b) show examples of its use. Figure 14.5(c) shows the application of a handrail bolt. The strong hexagonal-headed bolt, together with washers and timber connectors, will be dealt with in connection with roof trusses in volume 2.

14.4 Fixing plates
Figure 14.6 shows a few of the many fixing plates available. Some plates are multi-purpose, whereas others carry out specific functions; for example, movement plates have elongated slots to allow for either timber movement and/or fixing adjustment, glass plates act as a hanging medium for fixing items to walls, etc. Multi-purpose plates include angles, straights, tees, etc. to aid or reinforce various joints used in carcase construction.

Table 14.4 Threaded bolts

Bolt type	Material	Head	Nut and bolt	Application
Hexagonal head	S			Timber to timber; steel to timber (timber connectors etc.)
Coach bolt (carriage bolt)	S			Timber to timber; steel to timber (sectional timber buildings, gate hinges, etc.)
Roofing bolt	S, A			Metal to metal
Gutter bolt	S, A			Metal to metal
Handrail bolt	S			Timber in its length (staircase handrail, bay-window sill, etc.)

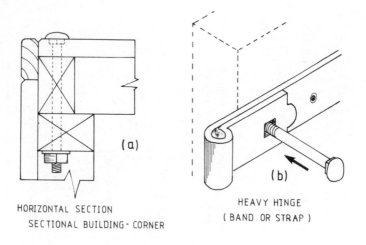

HORIZONTAL SECTION
SECTIONAL BUILDING- CORNER

HEAVY HINGE
(BAND OR STRAP)

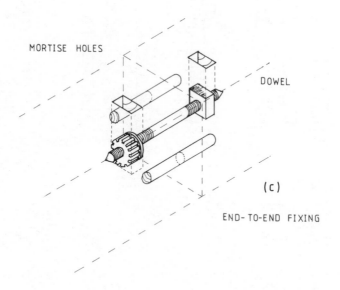

Fig. 14.5 Bolt application

There are also many different forms of metal straps, framing anchors, and joist hangers etc. which will be dealt with under the heading appropriate to their use, e.g. joist hangers are dealt with in connection with upper floors in volume 2.

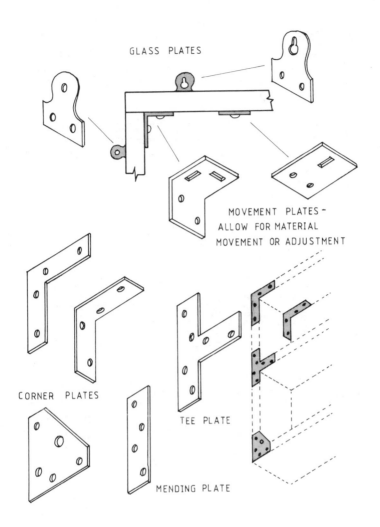

GLASS PLATES

MOVEMENT PLATES –
ALLOW FOR MATERIAL
MOVEMENT OR ADJUSTMENT

CORNER PLATES

TEE PLATE

MENDING PLATE

Fig. 14.6 Fixing plates

14.5 Plugs

Plugs are used where fixing directly to the base material is impracticable, for example because it is too hard, brittle, or weak. The type of plug or device used will depend on

a) the required strength of fixing;
b) the type, condition, and density of the base material to receive the plug;
c) whether fixing to a solid or a hollow construction.

A plug is either made from wood or purpose-made from a fibre, plastics, or metal material. The plug hole is bored either by hand, using a plugging chisel and hammer, or by machine, using a rotary or percussion drill (depending on the base material − see chapter 3) and a tungsten-carbide-tipped bit to suit the plug.

Wood plugs Figure 14.7 shows the shape, preparation, and fixing of a self-tightening plug. This method of plugging should not be used in situations such as those shown in fig. 14.8 − i.e. at a corner or head − because of the danger of wall disturbance.

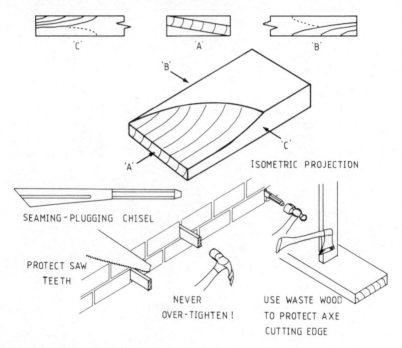

Fig. 14.7 Preparing and fixing wood plugs

Plastics plugs There is a selection of plastics plugs on the market to suit various base materials. These plastic materials, which include nylon and polythene, have very good holding characteristics and are unaffected by normal temperature change or corrosive conditions in the atmosphere. Figure 14.9 shows the use of a plastics Rawlplug.

Plugs are now available with the screw already encased inside. One type, known as the 'Rawlplug hammer screw', simply needs hammering through a pre-bored fixture into the plug hole, extra tightness or removal being achieved in the normal way with a screwdriver.

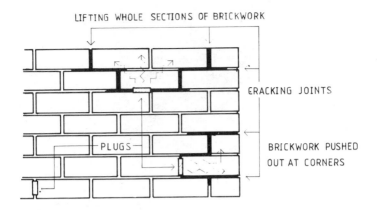

Fig. 14.8 Plugging situations to avoid

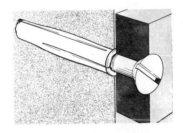

Fig. 14.9 Plastics 'Rawlplug'

Cavity fixings   These are useful for fixing to hollow or thin materials which are accessible from one side only. Typical situations include

a) hollow walls (building blocks),
b) hollow partitions (plasterboard),
c) wall panelling (plywood),
d) cellular flush doors (hardboard or plywood).

Rawlnut (fig. 14.10)   This is a flanged rubber sleeve which houses a nut and bolt. As the screw is tightened, the sleeve compresses against the back of the base material.

267

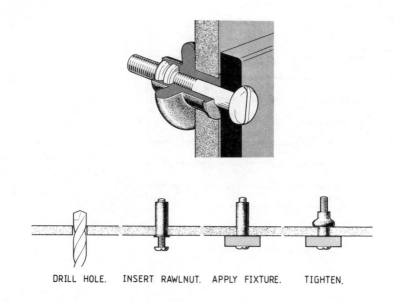

DRILL HOLE.   INSERT RAWLNUT.   APPLY FIXTURE.   TIGHTEN.

Fig. 14.10 'Rawlnut' and its application

Spring toggle (fig. 14.11)   This consists of a screw attached to steel spring wings which when folded back can be pushed through a hole into the cavity, where they spring apart and can then be drawn back against the base material by tightening the screw.

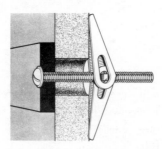

Fig. 14.11 'Rawlplug' spring toggle

Gravity toggle (fig. 14.12)   This is a metal channel fixed off-centre and allowed to swivel on a nut. When passed through a hole into a cavity, the channel hangs vertically and on tightening the screw the fixing becomes firm.

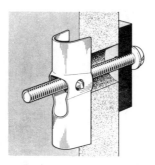

Fig. 14.12 'Rawlplug' gravity toggle

Rawlanchor (fig. 14.13)   A nylon plug is inserted into an 8 mm hole and, as the fixing screw is tightened, the plug compresses against the inside face of the cavity. This is an ideal device for shallow cavities.

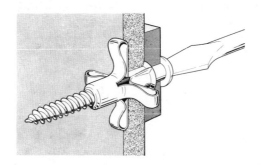

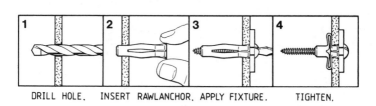

DRILL HOLE.   INSERT RAWLANCHOR. APPLY FIXTURE.   TIGHTEN.

Fig. 14.13 'Rawlanchor' and its application

Heavy fixings   These include bolts which expand on tightening while being held in an anchor hole (usually drilled in concrete). These devices are generally reserved for heavy structural work.

269

Index

271